Ordered Steps

ISBN 10: 1-933753-24-2
ISBN 13: 978-1-933753-24-9
All Scripture taken from King James Version

All text and poetry by Jessica Dorfsmith, unless otherwise noted.
Book Design by: Rosetta Mullet
Printed in the USA by Carlisle Printing of Walnut Creek

2673 Township Road 421
Sugarcreek, Ohio 44681

Carlisle Press
WALNUT CREEK

phone | 800.852.4482

ROCKY CEDARS ENTERPRISES
2140 Country Store Lane
Dayton, Virginia 22821
(540) 879-9714

Dedicated to:

My Lord and Savior,
who is my heart's greatest Treasure.

My parents,
who taught me to love the Lord
and yield to His hand.

My sister,
whose encouragement caused this book to be,
and whose friendship blesses my life.

My brothers,
who help me to balance my perspective
and keep a lively sense of humor.

Amanda,
for giving me good advice
and, inadvertently, the title for this book.

...Ordered Steps...

Introduction

Amy Carmichael, in her introduction to *Rose from Brier*, told how that poignant collection of "letters" was born out of the need for books written "by the ill for the ill." She explained from personal experience that material written by the well for those who suffer illness "does not do much for us. It can, indeed, be exceedingly irritating." Thus she compiled her treasure chest of encouragement for fellow "soldiers with another commission" from our heavenly Captain—that of physical pain.

Ordered Steps came about in much the same way, for much the same reason. Having spent my life-to-date single, I've had the opportunity to read many items written for single women. Very little material out there brings encouragement and purpose, simply because it is too often written by those who have never traveled far in the single lane. While I have gleaned helpful kernels from such writings (and there are a few perceptive writers I appreciate who, though married, have the ability to empathize), I must admit that a lot of the writings out there "do not do much for [me]." Sometimes they "can, indeed, be exceedingly irritating." Thus I have compiled, out of my own journey, what I hope to be a treasure chest of encouragement to my fellow soldiers with (for a season or a lifetime) "another commission" from our heavenly Captain—that of the single life.

This little book does not offer a polished masterpiece or claim to be an authority on the subject. As you read further, you will find that I am neither polished nor an authority! Also, not every entry will fit every reader, and some parts do not address the topic of singlehood at all—they simply reach out into the many facets of a Christian woman's life, married or single, young or old.

It is my prayer that this collection of simple, heartfelt poems and "letters" will fortify and inspire single women to honor and glorify our wonderful God, learning "in whatsoever state [we are], therewith to be content" (Philippians 4:11).

From one who has not attained, and yet by His grace I press on.

—*Jessica Dorfsmith*

Contents

> "…He will teach us of his ways,
> and we will walk in his paths."
>
> *Isaiah 2:3*

…Ordered Steps…

1

The Life of Ordered Steps

"Do you think something's wrong with me?" I asked half-seriously, looking across the small kitchen table at my friend. "Here I am, single as an odd sock—and I just turned 32 yesterday!"

I made a face, and Amanda laughed merrily, then sobered. "I don't mean to laugh, but you take such an extreme view of yourself," she chided, pouring me another cup of tea. "Of course there's nothing wrong with you, and you certainly aren't an 'odd sock'! You're one of the most enjoyable people to be with. If it's God's will for you to marry, you'll make His choice of a man very happy."

I gratefully smiled my thanks and took a sip of hot liquid. "I guess I'm just a little discouraged to see yet *another* year go by without those special hopes fulfilled," I admitted. "It's not that I lack fulfilling work and ministry—" I paused and grinned wryly. "But of course most women hope that God will give them some of His sweetest gifts: marriage, children, and a home to keep." I stroked Amanda's two-year-old daughter's curly head, and was rewarded with a dimpled smile before Katie toddled away to her toys.

"I know just how you feel." Amanda reached to squeeze my hand. "I struggled with those same emotions myself many times over the years—as you probably remember! I'm 30, and Philip and I have only been married for three years. But..." she paused. "Well, I must say that although wife- and motherhood are blessings, I wouldn't choose to have missed those single years. They were a growing time in my life that I'm grateful for—now that I see them in hindsight! I wish I would have valued them more at the time." She laughed softly, shaking her head in remembrance. "I can already see some of the reasons why waiting longer than usual for marriage was best for me, though. Looking back, I realize my single years had nothing to do with having 'something wrong' with me or whatever else to worry about! They were simply God-ordained."

God-ordained. The words hit me, clung to me, and have followed me ever since. There are times when I can easily grasp the restful fact that my heavenly Father plans life for me. But other times, like when a birthday rolls around, or a friend has their tenth wedding anniversary, or someone comments, "Oh! You aren't married? Why not?!", the peace of that knowledge eludes me and discouragement gnaws at my mind and emotions. Doubts bombard me. Did I accidentally fail somewhere and miss my "chance"? Am I living amid the wrong circumstances? I've always wanted to be a happy homemaker, so why doesn't God answer my prayers? Maybe even *He* thinks I'm not special enough! Is there really something wrong with me, after all? Suddenly I'm embarrassed to show my face in a world where so few are still single at 32.

This dark train of thought can cloud all of life's joy. But wait! If my

...Ordered Steps...

lot in life is truly *God-ordained*, then how can I find fault with it or be ashamed of it? The Bible tells me that God does all things well (Mark 7:37) and never makes a mistake (Deuteronomy 32:4). It promises that if I am yielded to Him and walking in obedience, He will order my steps (Psalm 37:23). It clears up all fear that God considers me of lesser value than others (John 3:16). It reminds me of the cross, and helps me to accept painful ordered steps.

Ordered steps? This truth illuminates my heart with joy. Too often we think of God's plans for us as something elusively future, a part of life to "look forward to." But when we remember that ordered steps mean an ever-present, right-this-minute type of walk, an in-His-will place to be, we discover the wonderful truth that we are living in God's plans for us *now*, this instant! Difficult or simple, painful or glad, our steps are God-ordained. Why, then, do I so often struggle?

The question makes me dig below the surface. What is the root of much struggle in our lives? Why do we murmur, doubt, or ask, "Why, Lord?" about anything? I've discovered the root in my life—it's an ugly word: *distrust*. Discontentment and asking "why" are always the offshoot of distrust. Distrusting God's wisdom, His promises, His purpose, and His plan is followed by discontentment, unhappiness, fear, and that relentless question, "Why?"

After my conversation with Amanda two whole years ago, I sought God earnestly for a new focus, a focus on *Him* above all. The word "God-ordained" spoke deeply to me about letting Him order my steps, my days, my years—not according to my own desires, but simply and only as He sees fit.

Am I now the joyful wife of a good man, contentedly keeping our own home? If so, you might shrug and say, "Ah, no wonder she speaks so boldly! See, God blessed her with all she desired. Of course she smiles now." But no, I am not married. There aren't even any remote possibilities on the horizon! Outwardly, not much has changed in the past twenty-four months. Yet I'm grateful to notice bright, glad changes inside! Clinging to the fact that, as a yielded child of God, He orders my steps, I experience a joy far deeper than I've ever known before. Instead of greeting each day with a sigh for what I *don't* have, I find myself rising eagerly to meet what God has planned for me. Instead of being wounded by the common idea that to be single at 34 denotes a "problem of some sort," I look up cheerfully to my God and say, "But we know that's not true, so who cares what misinformed people might think?!" And we walk on together in the path He chose for me today, undisturbed.

Does that mean my life is all roses now, without a ripple on the sea of peace? No! Unfortunately, I'm still bound in human clay and face as many battles as before, though perhaps different ones. But I'm grateful to find that I *have* grown. I've come to realize that the single life isn't something to be ashamed of if my all-wise, eternal God Almighty has placed me there. And I know I am not alone in the single state, today or in the past. Think of the Apostle Paul—he was single!

At the same time, never would I suggest that marriage and our desire for it is something to be ashamed of. Far from it! The same all-wise God who has called me to singlehood (perhaps only for a season), is the One who designed marriage. He does all things well. Married people aren't alone today or in the past. Remember the Apostle Peter? He was a married man.

But neither calling should distress us. Neither should it boost our pride or make us feel worthless. If we are living lives yielded to God, where we're at is *His* doing, not ours. We can take no credit or give no complaints. Let our daily focus be not on our circumstances, but rather on our heavenly Guide; content to do His will and daily walking in joyful surrender the life of ordered steps.

God Knows, God Sees

How well God knows,
How well He sees
The inner depths, the mysteries
That form my life, that trouble me—
GOD KNOWS, GOD SEES.

How well God plans!
How well He leads!
Guides through the darkness to the things
So clear to Him, though veiled to me—
GOD KNOWS, GOD SEES.

And since God knows,
And since He sees,
I can then trust, I can believe
That He who planned will pilot me—
GOD KNOWS, GOD SEES.

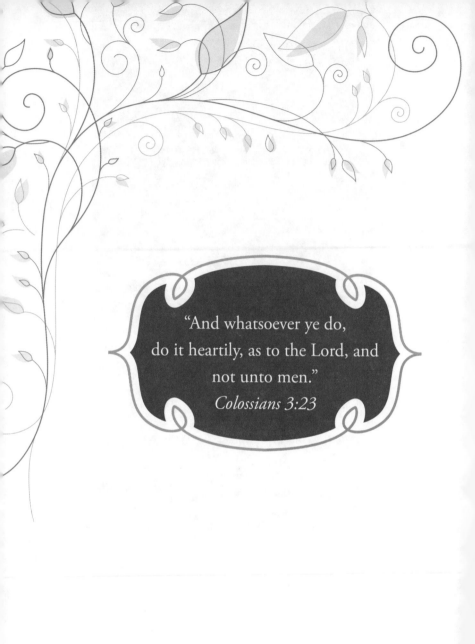

"And whatsoever ye do,
do it heartily, as to the Lord, and
not unto men."
Colossians 3:23

...Ordered Steps...

2

Ten Ways to Make YOUR DAY COUNT!

It's always sobering to stop in the midst of our mad rush of work and chores and ministry, and realize that we only have one life to live—and that life is made up of those little sections of time called "days"! How quickly they pass. Are we making each one count, even in the small areas? Longing to cherish each moment, I wrote this list for myself. It helps. Maybe you would like to try it too!

1. Don't skip prayer and Bible reading! This is your spiritual food—without it you will become undernourished and weak. Make your devotions the most meaningful part of your day! Get to know God's heart better through His Word, remember how very much He loves you, tell Him all about your life, and commit your day to His keeping. Purpose to live each moment heartily, as unto the Lord.

2. Choose to have a thankful outlook! Be on the alert for the good, not the bad. Count your blessings and rejoice and be glad in the day God has made—whether it's stormy or bright.

3. Find little ways to encourage or help someone, easing their burden. Write a note; share a smile; say a cheering word; send an uplifting poem, quote, or Bible verse—or simply be a listening ear.

4. Say hello to a child! Even if it's just an unknown little one you meet in the grocery store. There's nothing like a smile from a precious child to brighten your day and bless your heart!

5. Take time out for rest. Recognize that you are housed in human clay and won't ever be a superwoman! Make a cup of tea, put your feet up, and close your eyes. You'll be amazed at how it will improve your outlook—and, as a result, your entire day!

6. Sing a hymn! Find one that suits your need and let it be your theme song all through the day. You'll be amazed how it lifts your spirit and elevates your outlook!

7. Take time to enjoy nature, even if it's simply stopping to gaze at the vastness of the sky for a full minute. Let the grandeur of God's creation permeate your being, reminding you of His almighty power and perfect control.

8. Remember that as a single, focusing on "caring for the things of the Lord...without distraction" (I Corinthians 7:34-35) is your special privilege. Meditate on that thought and jot down ways you can focus your day more on the things of the Lord. Root out distractions that you are convicted of, such as shallow books, excessive time spent on hobbies, selfish use of your time, etc.

9. Have a healthy sense of humor. Look for truly funny things to laugh about—even if it happens to be yourself!

10. Give your daily work your best! Whatever your job, do it as unto the Lord and discover how fulfilling it can become!

...Ordered Steps...

This Day

I dedicate this day, dear Lord, to You.
Each little aspect, and each big, all through!
Give me the strength, give me the pow'r, I pray
To heartily live unto You this day.

Confidence

I lean my life on God,
My Father and my Friend;
My life, my very life
I lean on Him.
I trust to Him each moment,
Each step along the way—
He plans my tomorrows.
He planned today.

"…A woman that feareth the LORD, she shall be praised."

Proverbs 31:30

…Ordered Steps…

3

Beautiful

Potted plants grace the windowsill; delicate teacups line the hutch; a warm-toned crocheted throw hangs over the back of the wicker rocker; crisply laundered curtains frame the windows. Can't you tell that a woman—not a bachelor!—lives here?

I love beautiful things. Most women do! It seems to be something God included in our nature. We don't even have to be the dainty sort to have an inborn appreciation for loveliness. From a gorgeous sunrise, to an apple tree in fragrant bloom, we notice and enjoy.

Have you ever sensed how this natural bent makes us long for some of that beauty in our own person? We may inadvertently form in our mind's eye an idea of what we feel is especially lovely. Perhaps it includes long, dark eyelashes; a vibrant complexion; even teeth; and a tall, willowy figure. Unconsciously, we may notice those around us who have these features—then we happen to glance in the mirror and meet quite another sight! Suddenly we are plunged into discouragement. But we need to remember that each of us is created uniquely different, as diverse as a flower garden! Not every flower can compete with the elegant hybrid rose. And not every woman can fit into a certain standard for physical beauty. Yet deep inside is that inborn longing to be beautiful. What are we to do with it?

Beautiful. *The Webster's II New College Dictionary* defines it as, "Having qualities that delight the eye." How true! Vibrant hues of fall, soft tones of spring, a glistening mountain stream, an old painting, a bouquet of wildflowers in a cheery yellow pitcher—each draws our attention by first delighting the eye. We catch our breath in admiration and cry, "Oh, how beautiful!"

But what makes a woman beautiful? Worldly books and magazines burst with suggestions. Whole businesses devote their products toward that one aim. Yet a woman's quest for beauty can cause utter shipwreck of her life if she ignores the difference between true godly beauty and worldly vanity.

Referring back to *Webster's II* again, "vanity" is defined in part as, "The quality or state of being vain; excessive pride in one's appearance or accomplishments: conceit; something vain, futile, or worthless." The Bible warns us that the world's idea of womanly beauty is indeed vain and worthless. "Favour is deceitful, and beauty is vain: but a woman that feareth the LORD, she shall be praised" (Proverbs 31:30).

Vanity causes women to disregard their fear of God and eternity, desiring instead to draw the eyes of others to the fleeting charm of their outward appearance. How sad! Indeed, the world's brand of beauty is vain in the full definition of the word: both conceited and futile. So lies the snare into which many women become miserably entangled.

As Christian women, this should not happen to us! Yes, we desire to be beautiful, but the important question to ask ourselves is simply: "Whose eye am I striving to delight?" The answer should come spontaneously and joyously: "My Lord and Savior's eye, of course!"

What, then, is pleasing to the eye of God? What is the true definition of feminine beauty as specified by our Creator? We aren't left to guess—we have our very own beauty manual: God's Word! And encouraging and helping us along the way, we have the Holy Spirit's power in our lives. How wonderful!

Let's take a look at four main areas that delight the eye of God:

·*A Heart That Is Right with Him.* "But the LORD said unto Samuel, Look not on his countenance, or on the height of his stature;… for the LORD seeth not as man seeth; for man looketh on the outward appearance, but the LORD looketh on the heart (I Samuel 16:7).

We can have the trimmest of figures, the longest of lashes, and the charmingest of smiles, yet still not delight God's eye. His gaze penetrates further in. No one can be truly beautiful if there are bad attitudes, pride, evil thoughts, unforsaken sin, or rebellion inside. True beauty must start far below the surface. How is it with our hearts?

·*A Body That Brings Him Glory.* Since God looks on the heart, are obesity, neglect, poor grooming, and sloppiness acceptable? Or, on the other side of the coin, is it okay to follow after the vanity of the world in our outward appearance, if we try to keep our hearts right? I Corinthians 6:19-20 answers both questions: "What? know ye not that your body is the temple of the Holy Ghost which is in you, which ye have of God, and ye are not your own? For ye are bought with a price: therefore glorify God in your body, and in your spirit, which are God's."

If we were to invite beloved friends to our home, we would never give them a soiled, smelly, neglected chamber, or one fixed up in a way we know is particularly repugnant to them! How much more so should we strive for a healthy, well-groomed, modestly and neatly attired body, remembering just who it is that we have invited to live in us: the Holy Spirit of God! He deserves the best. Is the chamber of our body bringing Him glory?

·*Paying Attention to Detail.* What are a few examples in God's Word of what He considers true feminine beauty? Let's get out our magnifying glass and study the subject! A meek and quiet spirit; subjection to proper authority; modest apparel; shamefacedness; sobriety; good works; discreet; chaste; keeping the home; good; obedient; feminine (I Peter 3:3-4; I Corinthians 11:1-15; I Timothy 2:9-11, Titus 2:4-5; Deuteronomy 22:5; etc.). Nothing there about the shape of our nose, the size of our waistline, or the texture of our hair. And yet, each aspect listed above delights our Maker's eyes! Are we paying attention to these details?

·*A Reverent, Worshipful Fear of God.* We read earlier how, "Favour is deceitful, and beauty is vain: but a woman that feareth the LORD, she shall be praised" (Proverbs 31:30). True beauty springs from a reverent fear of God, causing us to love and obey Him. Do we have a proper fear of our amazing God?

Beautiful. The word holds far more meaning than first meets the eye, doesn't it?! But we don't have to get discouraged. Augustine once posed the question: "How shall we become lovely?" His answer holds the simple conclusion of the whole matter: "By loving Him who is ever lovely."

When we seek to love and obey our Lord in all ways, it will show, directing our thoughts, attitudes, speech, appearance, apparel, and actions. We will begin to see in every part of our lives a reflection of the One we love and follow. Now, *that* delights the eye of God—and it is beautiful!

Beauty Tips

·Want an all-over beautifier? Try Charles Dickens' tip:
*"Cheerfulness and contentment are great beautifiers and
famous preservers of good looks."*

·Truly casting your cares on the Lord effects an
immediate face-lift!

·*"The doing of common tasks patiently, promptly,
faithfully, cheerfully,"* wrote J.R. Miller *"…makes the
character beautiful and bright."*

· *"To grow in love, to lay aside self-seeking, and to live
for others,"* wrote Frances Paget, *"…alters even the tone
of [one's] voice and the look of [one's] face."*

· F.B. Meyer had a prayer for true beauty:
*"Mold us, great God, into forms of beauty and
usefulness by the wheel of Providence and by
the touch of Thy hand. Fulfill Thine ideal,
and conform us to the image of Thy Son."*

"…But God meant it unto good."
Genesis 50:20

…Ordered Steps…

4

Jason's Story

J ason was born blind. He has never watched the brilliant glow of a sunset. Never viewed a rugged mountain range or a meadow bright with wildflowers. Never looked into the faces of his loved ones. He cannot see.

But if you met him, you would be surprised at the smile on his face and the cheerfulness in his voice. Sightless eyes have not kept him from developing his talents or cultivating his other senses to useful service. His nimble, sensitive fingers craft well-made and beautiful furniture. His voice, melodious and deep, leads singing in a strong, God-glorifying way. His ears are tuned to listen to others who need someone to share their sorrows, struggles, or joys with. Like Beethoven who composed his most beautiful symphony, "Ode to Joy," after he became deaf, Jason has allowed his blindness to intensify his usefulness in life.

Was it an easy road to contentment? Did he ever struggle with accepting his fate? Jason will tell you that the road has not been an easy one. There have been deep rivers of discouragement to cross, hard climbs to accept God's will, and the ever-present desire to have his sight given to him. Two unsuccessful surgical attempts only ended in failure and heartbreaking disappointment. He has prayed often that God will heal him, but for a purpose of His own, God continues to answer, "Trust Me, child. My grace is sufficient."

Jason admits that hearing vivid descriptions about all he is missing out on is sometimes painful, filling him with an almost desperate longing to *see*. In a world where most people can see, he often feels alone, left out, and misunderstood.

But through the struggles Jason testifies that God is teaching him that joy is not dependent on sight, but is only found in surrender to His will and seeking a close relationship with Him. He is learning to focus on what he *does* have, not on what he lacks. He is learning to thrive in the place God has set him, satisfied with whatever God chooses and wherever He leads.

Has the desire for sight left him? No. Jason still wishes he could see. But the desire doesn't consume him any longer. "I'm learning to be like Fanny Crosby," he explains. "She rejoiced to realize that when she got to heaven, her first sight would be her Savior's face. Remembering that always brings unexplainable joy to my heart! My first sight will be Jesus—and it will be worth it all!"

Jason's story impacts my life as I compare it to my own story. No, I'm not blind, but in a world where the majority of people my age are married, I remain single.

I think there's a lot I can learn from Jason.

...Ordered Steps...

All Thine Heart

Trust in the Lord with all thine heart,
O HEART OF MINE;

Thine understanding falleth short
OF HIS DESIGN.

His will for thee is just and good—
HE IS ALL-WISE;

His way cannot be understood,
YET IT IS RIGHT.

So trust the Lord with all thine heart,
O HEART OF MINE;

Most precious blessings He'll impart
IN HIS OWN TIME.

> "...Godliness with contentment
> is great gain."
> *I Timothy 6:6*

...Ordered Steps...

5

The Womanly Art
OF HOMEMAKING

It is the godly woman's joy and commission to make her home into a comfortable, lovely retreat for her family. A "homemaker" is defined as, "One who manages a household." And "household" means, "A domestic establishment including the members of a family and others who live under the same roof."

I've always looked forward to the privilege of homemaking! But as the years went by and I remained single, reality told me that I may never have a true home to make comfortable, or a family of my own to find retreat there. It was a daunting thought! I imagined the lovely items in my hope chest rotting away until, sixty-some years down the road, future grandnieces and nephews would auction them off to strangers, who would display the then-antique items in a comfortable home somewhere. How depressing!

I've learned a lot since then! A woman doesn't have to have a family all her own before she can turn her house (or room, trailer, apartment, etc.) into a homey bower of comfort and beauty. And just because she doesn't have "family members and others" living under the same roof, doesn't mean she cannot make a lovely establishment for herself. And so what if she didn't marry by thirty? That doesn't mean her hope chest is doomed to collect dust in her parents' attic! There is no reason why she must be barred from the womanly art of making a lovely home, merely because she is single. This, at least, has been my personal discovery.

As a single in my thirties, I admit that there have been moments of feeling like I'm living in a "holding tank," waiting for my Knight in Shining Armor to release me and usher me into "real living." But God only gives us today. He wants us to live—really *live*, and to the fullest, for His glory!—right now. It's the unfulfilling and depressing "waiting for someday" attitude that gives singlehood such a sour flavor—especially if our "someday" never comes!

But why settle for snacking on the sour apples of what we *don't* have, when there are some wonderfully sweet tidbits we *do* have within our reach? Inadvertently we sometimes buy into the "left on the shelf" misconception of the single life, where life stretches out before us like a cold, monotonous road. We look at homey joys as belonging only to those whom God has given a husband and family.

Of course some of those joys *are* reserved for married couples, but some are available to all women. Why miss out?! Nowhere in the Bible do we find anything stating that a single woman shouldn't glory in the art of homemaking, perfecting her cooking skills, and letting her own personal brand of decorating make a comfortable retreat for herself and her visitors.

This womanly way of life helps keep our spirits gentle, feminine, and sweet. Then, if God chooses not to send us a husband, we won't get frozen into stereotypical spinsterhood, but instead will be warmhearted, content, happy women living vibrant, fulfilling lives—wherever God places us! Mind if I share a few points that have given me much sweetness and homey joy?

1. Cultivate a content spirit, yielded to God's will. Not sighing over what we've missed, or looking ahead toward the possibilities of the future; instead, purposefully seeking to find joy within the sphere God has placed us *today*.

2. Give your "house" a complete makeover. Clear out everything, scrub from top to bottom, and start fresh! Discard useless clutter. If you can, give the walls a coat of paint—it's amazing what a cheery transformation this brings!

3. Use your imagination and rejuvenate your decor. It doesn't have to cost a fortune to make your place homey! Quilt new valances from scrap material; cover old pillows with pretty prints from the bargain rack; line a sunny windowsill with houseplants; rearrange your furniture to make your space as convenient and cozy as possible. Try your hand at painting or stenciling verse motto plaques—they add such an uplifting atmosphere!

4. I've found that a wonderful way to make my apartment homey is to have a special easy chair for myself. Save up your money and keep on the lookout for bargains! After a hard day's work, there's nothing quite so relaxing as a comfortable chair!

5. Open that hope chest and put those treasures to use! During my teenage years, it was special to create useful, pretty items for my future home. I made quilts, afghans, doilies, wall hangings, Scripture mottoes, pillow covers, dish towels, and more. It was a good learning experience and a profitable way to fill my free time. With a tender

smile and rose-colored dreams, I packed each item away with dried lavender—waiting for that glorious "someday" when I would (of course!) marry and have a home of my own.

It never occurred to me back then that the day might come when I would have a place of my own (even though it's only an apartment above my parents' garage)—without the husband part! But as the years galloped by, I could have kept all of those items packed away, a useless monument to my girlhood dreams that (as yet!) have not come true. But I didn't! I've discovered how truly homey and cozy my hope chest items make a house—even though it belongs only to me! (Oh, and by the way, my hope chest itself makes a nice coffee table!)

6. Be hospitable! If you have the room, invite family members, friends, single girls, elderly couples, widows. Let them enjoy the comfortable coziness of your homey retreat! Don't worry about having everything "just so"—relax and let your home be inviting, not a stiff and formal "showpiece."

If you wonder how to keep company entertained, here are a few suggestions: Invest in profitable "coffee table" books, such as Pablo Yoder's *The Work of Thy Fingers* and *My Father's World*. Keep a container full of building blocks, good books, puzzles, and other toys for your small guests. Or plan events at your home that will keep everyone occupied with a worthwhile project, such as sewing quilts or baby layettes for charity organizations, putting together food parcels for needy families, etc. If some events include the husbands or brothers of your friends, ask your father or a family member to act as host.

7. Don't neglect your cooking skills just because you know you can't eat "all that" alone! There will always be someone to appreciate the extra cinnamon rolls, the greater part of that casserole, and the rest of that pot of stew! Share with busy mothers, elderly couples, or needy people in your congregation. It has been my experience that

cooking and baking for others gives a woman a fulfilled, useful feeling that is all a part of simple womanly joys. Life has been much more meaningful since I've posed the question: "Why cheat myself out of all these blessings just because I'm not married?"

I'm still keeping my eyes open for more ways to glory in the womanly art of homemaking as a single. It certainly is a wonderful change from the "left on the shelf" way of life! And if you haven't already embarked on this pleasant voyage yourself, I invite you to climb aboard and find out just how good it is!

The Single Homemaker

There are homes God-blessed with a family,
Husband and a wife, children, unity.
It can make my home seem so dark and drear—
Yet God put me here.

Centered in His will: the best place to be!
Though He's filled my home with just only me.
To devise my way is a thing to fear—
I'll be thankful here.

There are homes I've viewed that are cold and grim,
Housing stormy hearts void of joy; and then
With a prayer of thanks, I can see it clear:
God has blessed me here.

There's a braided rug on the hearth below
Where a cheery fire gives a homey glow;
And a pleasant chair has been drawn up near—
You will find me here

With a book in hand, and a cup of tea
In the quiet nook of my home retreat.
And the world outside cannot interfere—
God is Master here.

...Ordered Steps...

Content

Today is all our Father God has given
For us to take, and open as a gift,
And use in ways to bring Him praise and glory—
Remember this.

And even if the gift is one of trials—
Sharp-sided, cutting, and a mystery,
He still expects His child to take and use it
Resourcefully.

And if we find that things aren't to our liking,
Life hasn't gone in our requested bent;
Instead our Father's time and plan is different—
Let's be content.

For leaning on His strength and power to do it,
No self-pity, no "how I wish I had…"
Will blur our goal of bringing God the glory.
Let us be glad!

Living in contentment doesn't mean leaving off praying for our deepest desires. Instead, it means committing them into the hands of the One who made us, and trusting them there. Often, it is in the thick of the battle or during the common daily work that God surprises us with joy—and sends a blessing *far beyond our dreams!*

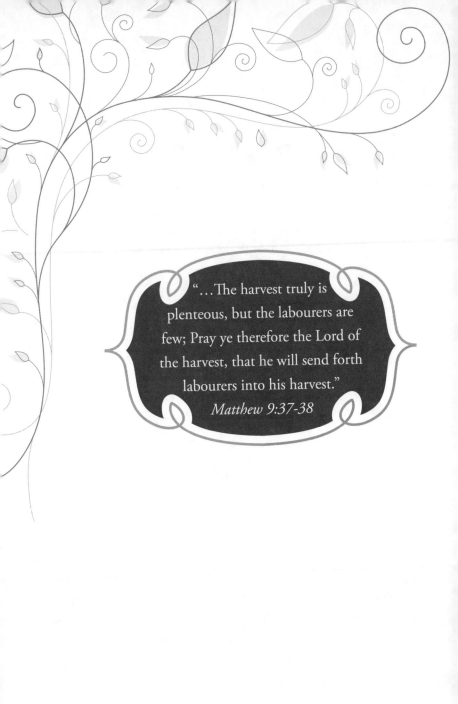

"…The harvest truly is plenteous, but the labourers are few; Pray ye therefore the Lord of the harvest, that he will send forth labourers into his harvest."

Matthew 9:37-38

6

There Were Only a Few

Rays of light spilled across the morning as the sun crested the horizon. I stepped out into the early coolness, marveling at the beauty of the soft, blue sky and the fragrant breeze that carried the scent of roses. I turned my steps down a long road, lined the entire way by vast, ripe fields as far as the eye could see. It would be a good day for such a walk. I could picture already the sight that would meet my eyes. There would be hundreds of men working in earnest haste; laboring to bring the harvest in, shouting words of encouragement to each other, and filling the air with songs of thanksgiving—for, indeed, the harvest was great.

But in the vastness of the fields, I could spot no one at work— wait! There, almost obscured from view, was one man. He worked diligently, yet drooped from weariness.

As I continued, I could see a scattering of laborers. How they toiled! And yet—oh, those vast, vast fields! These few could never finish the work without help.

It was then that I noticed other men milling about in the fields. Some were dressed in work clothes, others in their Sunday best, but all seemed to be out simply for a stroll in the sunshine. From time to time the few men busy at work would call to these idle ones, "Come and help us! Look! The day is passing quickly—and there is so much to be done!" Some of the idle men would smile and wave as they passed by. Some ignored the call completely, intent on chasing rabbits through the fields or chatting about the view. Others openly scoffed, replying that with so much work to be done, their small help would be pointless. And yet I knew, as I looked across the fields at them all, that if each man would do his part, much could be accomplished! Occasionally one of these loiterers would realize the urgency of the need and roll up his sleeves, joining in the effort. Yet most did not.

The sun was now overhead. As I gazed about searchingly, I saw, here and there, other people busily bringing refreshment to the scattering of laborers. They seemed to give the harvesters renewed strength and fresh hope as they encouraged them. By this I knew to count them among the laborers, for all were joining efforts to bring in the harvest. And yet there were so few.

Now the sun was lowering towards the west. Shadows were lengthening across the fields. In sharp, stinging surprise, I saw a man from among the laborers beckoning to *me*. "Come and help us!" he urged. "The night quickly approaches, and there is still so much to be done." I looked at the toilworn figure of the man, how he was bowed under the work, and yet his face glowed with eagerness and joy. I thought of how much I would have to give up if I were to join in the labor. No longer would I be able to take a relaxing stroll, secure in the safety and ease of observing from afar. Labor meant effort, tears, and sweat. Was I willing?

...*Ordered Steps*...

Suddenly I saw the toilworn man turn to the laborers gathered among the fields, and cry out, "Remember what our Master said! 'The harvest truly is plenteous, but the labourers are few; Pray ye therefore the Lord of the harvest, that he will send forth labourers into his harvest.'" And there arose a mighty sound of prayer.

Then it seemed as if the great Master Himself called to me, and the urgency of His voice reached my very heart. No longer could I merely watch from afar. Earnestly I rolled up my sleeves and went running to the fields. The day was quickly passing and there was still much work to be done. With the call of the Master in my ears, I would do my part.

Thy Laborer

I do not want to be a stagnant pool;
River of Love, I want to be like Thee;
Deep, abundant, flowing, ever full:
Thou as my Source—might I Thy channel be?
O flow, River of Love, flow Thou through me.

I do not want to dwell on things trivial,
O Word of Life, I want to speak of Thee.
Thou, O Lord, art Life, Thy touch doth heal,
Surrounding are the sick, the lost, the weak—
O speak, Thou Word of Life, speak Thou through me.

I do not want to be a slow pupil—
O Teacher, I would quickly learn from Thee!
Thy lessons are the delight of my soul—
Help me to better learn so all may see,
O teach, Thou great Teacher, teach Thou through me.

But I am such a small and frail child, Lord!
My spirit willing—O, my flesh so weak!
Refine with fire; prune with Thy sharp Sword;
So not my weakness, Lord, will others see,
But Thy powerful Flame indwelling me. Amen.

Tools

A cup of water, cold and pure,
A helping hand, a listening ear,
A firm rebuke, a gentle prod,
May lead a sinner home to God.

A peaceful life, a loving deed,
A seasoned word, a planted seed,
A meek confession when we fall
May help recall a prodigal.

A faithful walk, a love that's strong,
A fervent prayer, a joyful song,
Though slight and small, these tools may be
Harvesting for eternity!

God calls each of us to labor, for the harvest is truly plentiful. *What is your part?* Consider the gifts and talents He has given you, the circumstances He has set you in, the people He has surrounded you with, the places that He may be calling you to. This is your field and there is so much to be done! Perhaps you are already busy among the harvesters—*or is it time to roll up your sleeves?*

"I delight to do thy will, O my God: yea, thy law is within my heart."
Psalm 40:8

"…The will of the Lord be done."
Acts 21:14

…Ordered Steps…

7

To Glory in the Will of God

"Look for red maples on the left," Laura reminded herself, touching the brakes and squinting through the windshield at the south side of the highway. A bright glow of autumn red among yellow and orange cottonwoods dazzled her eyes. "This must be the place," she murmured, easing her car onto the long, maple-lined driveway.

She caught her breath at the view opening before her. What a lovely setting—so picturesque! A little thrill of pain mixed with her joy in the beauty of the twenty-minute drive over. No wonder Sadie and Trent were enthusiastic! Wasn't this so much like what she herself often dreamed of? The gently rolling fields nestled against wooded hills, the large farmhouse surrounded by maples and oaks, the well-kept red barn blending with the autumn colors, and a fork of the river winding through cottonwoods to the west of the driveway. It was a charming scene.

Laura swallowed hard. "Lord," she prayed simply, "help me to rejoice in others' joys—even though my blessings are quite different than theirs!" Gentle peace spread warmly through her and the quiet joy returned. It was a lesson learned over years of struggle—those quick little prayers. And God was always faithful to hear and answer.

Now she found herself smiling as she took in the view. It was wonderful how the Lord had given her cousin's family this small farm—the result of years of prayer and hard work! After a bit of repair on the old house, the family hoped to move in during the next two weeks. Laura glanced at the early morning blue of the October sky. How nice that Sadie and Trent would be settled before winter! But there was still much to be done.

Today's project centered around repainting the kitchen and dining room. "Trent asked if I could do the inside painting so he wouldn't have to take off work," Sadie had remarked after church the week before. "But with no helpers and all of my little ones underfoot, I'd be cleaning up more spilled paint than anything else. I know you do a nice job of painting—whether it be walls or plaques! Would you mind helping?" And Laura had gladly agreed. It would be fun to help put a pretty cream color over the drab green walls Sadie had described.

Now, as she parked near the house, she glimpsed a slender figure coming out to the porch, waving an unused stir stick and smiling cheerily. Laura chuckled, returning the exuberant wave. It looked like Sadie had commandeered her youngest sister Bethany's help as well. Bethany's bubbly personality would certainly add to the enjoyment of the day!

"Hello!" she greeted the younger girl heartily, stepping out of the car and pulling the lever to open the trunk. "So your sister got you to help too, did she?"

Bethany laughed merrily as she came down the porch steps and to

...Ordered Steps...

the back of Laura's car. "Yes, little sisters come in handy, it seems. And cousins, too! I'm glad you're here. Sadie's putting Samuel down for his nap, and the other children are *supposed* to be scrubbing the cellar floor," she explained. "Since Trent did all the sanding and masking last night, I was just about ready to open a can of primer and get started. Here, let me take some of that!"

Laura hid her amusement as Bethany stopped the chatter just long enough to take a large paper bag and peek inside. "Yum, some of your delicious canned vegetable soup—and homemade rolls, too! Is this our dinner?"

"It sure is, along with the block of cheese and jar of apple juice in this bag," Laura said, matching her shorter steps to Bethany's energetic stride. "Also, Sadie said there are still potatoes and salad greens in the garden that we can use. I told her not to worry about cooking—I'd take care of that today."

"Thanks! Mother sent some cookies along too, so we'll be dining in style," Bethany enthused. "And Trent had the propane tank filled yesterday, plus got the cellar stove in working order. We're all set!"

They entered the house, and Bethany led the way to a folding table set up in the living room. After depositing their packages there, Laura looked around with interest.

"Nice and spacious—perfect for a growing family," she commented. "Oh, and look at how large the south windows are! I love big windows—especially with a view like that!" She drew a deep breath at the beauty and smiled. "I've always had a warm spot in my heart for old farmhouses."

Bethany cast her a curious look. "Really? I guess it's hard for me to picture you anywhere but in that cute little trailer at your parents' place."

Laura gave a little laugh. "Actually, it's only been eight years since

Dad set that trailer up for me," she remembered. "But then, I guess you were only about ten when I moved over there. That probably seems like ages ago to you—but it seems like yesterday to me! Okay," she interrupted herself briskly, "where are those children? I must give hugs and kisses before I can start working!"

Heading down the cellar steps, Laura found herself shaking her head. It still felt funny at times to think that her thirty-year-old cousin Sadie, five years younger than she was, had a house full of little ones and a six-month-old baby. Life held surprises she certainly hadn't anticipated when she was a dreamy girl of Bethany's age! Why, she had been seventeen when Bethany was born. She could still remember holding the warm, cuddly bundle and thinking, with an eager anticipation in her heart, that it wouldn't be many years before it was her turn to have a bundle all her own. But that was eighteen years ago—and she remained single. God's plans were sometimes far different than her own.

Not that she had completely erased the possibility of marriage from her mind. God could sometimes surprise you with special joys! Hadn't her good friend Grace married happily at 38? Now Grace had that dear little bundle all her own—she'd just had to wait longer than most! But Laura didn't live in the expectation of that "just around the corner" for herself. She had learned over the years that the best way to keep out discouragement was to lay those desires in God's hands, committing her future to Him with a simple, "The will of the Lord be done."

The cellar was definitely convenient, with rows of shelves and a work space near the stove for canning or other projects. After rescuing three-year-old Johnny from a pool of sudsy water, kissing four-year-old Rose and six-year-old Emma's eager faces, and praising eight-year-old Sarah for the progress on the grimy concrete floor, Laura

...Ordered Steps...

went back up the stairs and searched for the kitchen. She followed the murmur of voices, and found Sadie and Bethany stirring primer and getting out paint supplies.

"Good morning, Sadie!" she greeted, stepping in the doorway and glancing around admiringly. "So much room in here! I hope you won't get lost after being used to that tiny kitchen in your rented place."

"I might!" Sadie agreed laughingly, her blue eyes sparkling in her pleasant round face. "I'm so thankful for this big kitchen—and for *you*, coming to help cover up this ugly green! Here, choose your weapon: a roller or a paintbrush?"

"A roller, please! Don't you girls know rollers work best for large surfaces, while those little brushes will be perfect for cutting in corners and doing trim?" Laura teased.

Sadie and Bethany looked at each other sheepishly. "I *knew* you invited her for a reason," Bethany said in a mock whisper to Sadie, exchanging her brush for a roller.

Sadie grinned. "Now that I think of it, Trent *did* tell me to use the rollers for the walls. Thanks, Laura! Left to ourselves, we'd make quite a mess!"

A comfortable silence settled over them as they filled roller trays and each chose a wall to begin on.

"This looks better already—and it's only the primer!" Laura remarked after fifteen minutes of vigorous application. "Oh, there's a cry from the bedroom! Shall I get Samuel?"

"Well… I'd better get him," Sadie decided, shaking her head and laying aside her roller. "He's having trouble cutting teeth, poor darling, and doesn't seem to settle down for anyone but me." She glanced at her watch. "I should check on the other children, too. You girls keep on—it's looking good!"

As Sadie bustled out of the room, Laura smiled at Bethany. "She's a busy woman! She told me on the phone this morning that she was up late last night, getting the cellar shelves washed while Trent worked in here."

"I know!" Bethany sighed. "Poor Sadie. Did you notice those circles under her eyes? She doesn't get much sleep, what with Samuel teething and Johnny's cough last week. Then all of the repair here, and the packing at their old place—ouch! But I'm sure it's worth it. Still, I'm glad we're helping with painting. It's good you were able to get a free day today!"

Laura ran her roller through the paint tray and pressed off excess paint, mounting the stepladder. "That's what I like about my job," she said. "It's flexible, giving me the opportunity to help others when I'm needed."

She painted several rows in silence. Yes, it was moments like these that she enjoyed being single—free to choose her schedule and let the Lord lead. At first she hadn't been at all enthused with the idea of starting a housecleaning business among the church families. But she had yielded to her parents' suggestion and, over the years, had actually learned to enjoy the job. She found herself laughing softly as she moved the stepladder and began another row.

"I was just thinking that I've been doing housecleaning jobs for almost ten years now," she explained at Bethany's questioning look. "It seems amazing! I never imagined it would grow into a full-time business. But I'm thankful for the work God supplies."

"Ten years of housecleaning jobs—whew! But remember your writing," Bethany added. "You forgot to mention that you write for several publications, Miss Author."

Laura smiled as she descended the ladder to pour more primer in her tray. "I do enjoy *that* more than housecleaning," she admitted. "But it only takes up part of my time right now and doesn't pay much.

Maybe someday I'll be able to support myself through writing alone, though—who knows what God has planned? He is always faithful to lead to what's best! I think that is one of the sweetest lessons the Lord has been teaching me—how faithful He is."

Laura felt Bethany's curious gaze again. "You should see how illuminated your face is at that thought!" she said half-wistfully. "But you talk like— Well, I mean, it seems like you enjoy life a lot, even though you don't have a family of your own. I'm sure I couldn't!"

Laura blinked. There it was again—that little thrill of pain; that sting in her heart at the realization of how different her life was from most women her age. She didn't have what she had always dreamed of, but God *had* given her much to be thankful for. Still, of course Bethany couldn't understand that yet. Laura swallowed hard and sent up a quick prayer. How could she explain to a girl of eighteen the discipline of seventeen extra single years? Yes, sometimes life hurt—badly. But how could she express God's peace, even amid the battles of daily accepting His will?

She could understand Bethany's feelings. In a way singlehood had been even more frightening when she was younger. "Help me to say the right thing, Father!" she prayed silently.

"There are a lot of things I enjoy about being single," she acknowledged. "I try to count my blessings every day. It helps keep me content, even without a family of my own."

At the doubtful look in Bethany's blue eyes, she went on. "I guess it has to do with cultivating a love for the will of God. When I see busy moms like Sadie—without a moment to themselves!—I try to remember to be grateful for the luxury of time God gives me as a single. If God sends marriage, of course I'll adjust myself to *that* way of life. But He hasn't yet, so I have to count my blessings where I'm at."

She stopped to gather her thoughts. "As a single, I don't have the demands of a family pulling me in a dozen different directions at once," she said slowly. "I'm not up nights with teething infants or sick children; I'm not consumed with the vast number of motherly duties. Not that I'd turn any of that down! But since I don't have it, I *do* have time to invest for the Lord in different ways—and yes, I've learned to enjoy that!" The reminder brought a glow to her eyes and a smile to her face.

"But wait a minute!" Bethany protested. "Probably you don't mean to, but you seem to be glorifying singlehood and downplaying the blessings of wife- and motherhood. Sure, marriage and all that has its hard parts, but it doesn't mean we shouldn't want it! I guess you've never felt the way I do."

Laura's eyes widened and her busy hands slowed to a stop. "Oh, I don't mean to glorify singlehood," she said earnestly. "I'm sorry if it sounded that way! In fact, I still hope to someday marry, if the Lord wills. But I guess what I'm trying to say is that, although I've struggled through painful times of longing for a family of my own, not all of us are given that blessing at the same age—and some of us never are! So we must yield those desires to God, because," she finished softly, "every one of us is called to be content where He places us today."

She chuckled at the serious look on Bethany's face. "You don't need to worry about singlehood, girlie," she said with a smile. "You've got plenty of time yet."

"Not really," Bethany protested, her usually cheerful face clouded with pain. "Look at my friend Ruth Ann. She's getting married in the spring, and she's just nineteen! I don't even have a young man interested in me yet—that I know of. I'll be nineteen in three months. It makes me feel like my time is running out!"

"Ah, but," Laura said in a low tone, "into whose hands have you committed your time?"

Bethany looked confused, then a blush spread over her face. "Into

...Ordered Steps...

God's hands, of course," she said softly. "But it's still hard."

There was a rustle in the doorway, and Sadie entered with rosy-cheeked Samuel on her hip. She smiled from Laura to Bethany. "I heard a lot of talking in here, so I didn't expect much progress—but I was wrong! You've done well. I sent the children to dig potatoes. Shall we take a break for a cup of tea, and then start dinner when the children come in?"

Laura and Bethany chorused agreement, putting away their paint supplies and going to the cellar where a teakettle was boiling merrily on the stove.

"So, what was the all-consuming topic before I interrupted?" Sadie asked, once they were settled on folding chairs in the living room, sipping hot tea.

"We were talking about marriage versus the single life," Bethany told her. "But I still can't *quite* see Laura's point of view. Especially about giving up our desires for marriage and being happy even as a single." She laughed ruefully and gave Laura an apologetic look over the rim of her teacup. "I'm glad Laura's happy, but I doubt if I'd ever find anything good about being single."

In answer to Sadie's raised eyebrows, Laura chuckled and related their conversation.

"I'll add the perspective of a married woman," Sadie said. "I'm not ashamed to say I'm glad God placed me where He has—even though it isn't all roses, I can tell you! But yes, I do love my position in life. At the same time, it's wonderful to see how our faithful Lord helps Laura find fulfillment and joy in singlehood, despite the un-rosy aspects. God wants us to be content wherever we are."

"Oh sure, I know *that*," Bethany agreed. "And I'm not wanting you to go around with a long face, Laura! You're wonderful as you are, which is why I like being with you so much. But I guess I'm thinking of myself. Marriage is my biggest dream—and I love children! It's biblical, too. God ordained it. So, shouldn't we all get it if we want it? Wouldn't God take away those desires if He didn't have marriage in His plan for us?"

Laura smiled at Bethany's innocent conclusion. "Give us your input, Sadie," she said, taking chubby little Samuel from Sadie's arms and cuddling him close. "I'll take a break and listen in."

"Oh dear, I'm put on the spot without time to prepare!" Sadie laughed. "Umm, let me think a minute. Well, here's where I think the main point lies: we should never lift up marriage as something to be... well, worshiped, I guess is the word. Whether we marry or not isn't up to the yielded child of God—He decides that for us. We should simply trust God's choice, whatever it may be, and for however long the season. And," she added, "just because God puts us somewhere doesn't mean it will be easy for us to be content there. That's where His grace comes in."

She paused, tears filling her eyes. "God works in ways we can't understand, Bethany, dear," she said gently. "You know how Mom found such joy in being Dad's wife. But when God called Dad home three years ago, Mom didn't let her emotions and sorrow control her. She yielded to the Lord. I doubt if He took away her feelings, but He *did* give her grace to cope. And even to find joy and purpose in life again."

"That's basically my point," Laura interjected, her heart thrilling with the depth of Sadie's words. She looked kindly at Bethany's troubled face. "To be put on a certain path doesn't mean the terrain won't be hard. But if we yield to God's will, neither will it be miserable. In fact, it will be permeated with joy since *God* has placed us there and walks beside us. He scatters blessings all along the way—I know that from experience." She set her empty teacup on the table, then went on thoughtfully, "Recognizing and being thankful for those blessings fills

us with peace. That's why we don't have to worry about *what* His will might be. He'll take care of us, whatever He chooses!"

She laughed softly as a new thought came to her. "All of this is a process! The Apostle Paul grew so content in the single state that he could even say he wished *all* men were like him. I haven't progressed that far! There are still times when I feel that I absolutely can't go on single another day, and wouldn't wish such torture on anyone!" Laura kissed the top of Samuel's fuzzy head and felt tears fill her eyes. "I go through bouts of fasting and prayer," she admitted, "asking God for a good husband and for dear little ones like this. I freely admit I've experienced doubt and disappointment when God doesn't give what I ask for."

"That's just how I feel—like I can't go on without marriage much longer, and that surely God will answer if I pray hard enough!" Bethany confessed. "But I guess I didn't imagine you ever experienced that, Laura. Why, I've read in books by trustworthy authors that if you feel that way, it means you are *not* called to be single. They say that only people who don't experience those desires are called to the single life—right?"

Laura had to laugh. "Wrong!" she insisted. "Those folks obviously never walked far in the single lane. If I can speak for most of my single friends and for myself, I'll tell you that God gives every healthy woman the desire for marriage and children. It's like—like..." she paused, then went on. "Well, think of a person who has an accident and gets paralyzed. I doubt if we'd say, 'Ah, he must not have the same desire to walk as I do, or God wouldn't have allowed that!'"

She shook her head. "God doesn't work that way. I've learned that whenever He allows something difficult in our lives, it is a spiritual discipline in which His grace alone is sufficient."

She shifted the squirming baby to her other shoulder, patting his back. Bethany's earnest young face and Sadie's sweet, tired eyes touched her heart. "Each part of life has its spiritual disciplines," she mused aloud. "Teenagers, wives, mothers, singles, widows. That's why it's so important to—" she paused again, letting the beauty of the truth fill her heart before continuing softly, "to daily glory in the will of God in our lives. *That* is our calling, and nothing more." She thought of her earlier struggles that day and sighed. "If only I could always remember that in my own life!"

Silence covered the little group while the words sank in. "You're right—that fits any path God calls us to," Sadie agreed. "What a lovely truth! I need to have a motto with that above my kitchen sink!"

Bethany drew a deep breath and let it out in a sigh. "You've given me a lot to think about, big sister—but especially *you*, Miss Author!" She grinned at Laura, and Laura felt relief at the brightening glow on the younger girl's face. "I can tell you're a true writer," Bethany went on. "You put your point across in a way that stabs my heart!" She laid her hands dramatically over her heart and looked playfully at Laura. But there was a new peace in her eyes. "I'm thinking of a verse," she added. "In Psalms, I believe. It says something like, 'I delight to do thy will, O my God.' I guess God's will for me today is just to be happy as an almost-nineteen-year-old, delighting to do whatever He sends my way. See?" she grinned at them. "I'm not such a giddy youth after all! Oh, and Laura, could you paint that verse and your neat saying on a motto for me for my birthday? *Seriously*," she said, as Laura and Bethany smiled at each other. "I mean it. I think it will help me to be reminded of that every day."

"I'll make one for each of us," Laura agreed heartily, rising to open the door for the exuberant group of children trooping up the porch steps. "Even though I coined the saying, I still need to be reminded of the truth behind it—and that lovely verse! Now, how about you two getting back to work while Samuel and I put dinner on? It's nearly twelve o'clock!"

...Ordered Steps...

Trusting the One Who Knows

The Lord above, wonderfully strong,
Can do no wrong.

If He should choose this path to lead
Thy soul along,

Know it is right; cease now thy fight
And raise thy song

To God above, wonderfully strong,
Who does no wrong.

The Planning

Go lay it in the hands of God the Father.
Remember that you are His own—His daughter!
And trust it to His care, He cannot fail—
His purpose will most certainly prevail.

So rest! It is not up to you—the planning
Is up to God; cease striving and demanding.
The best that He can give you He's preparing—
Go lay it in the hands that know no erring.

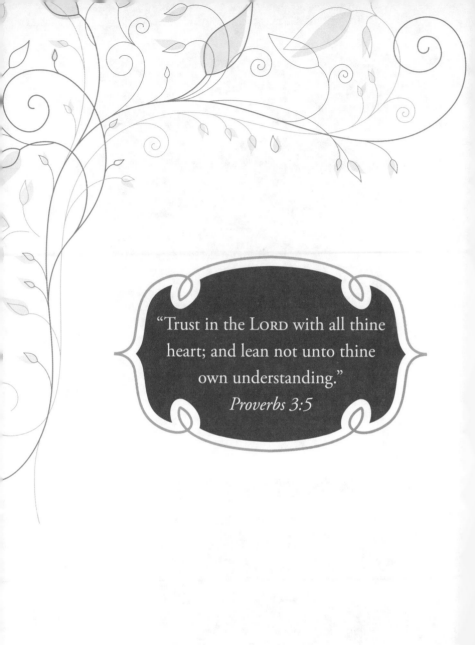

"Trust in the LORD with all thine heart; and lean not unto thine own understanding."

Proverbs 3:5

...Ordered Steps...

8

Unanswered

Reading the Book of the Acts of the Apostles always ignites a fire of awe in my heart. The awesome power of God is revealed so magnificently! I read with bated breath of healings, signs, and wonders revealed in a way we don't experience in our time. What a thrilling era that must have been! Since I'm faced with physical problems, I sometimes think longingly of the period when God allowed His power to work so forcefully through human clay, that the mere touch of Peter's shadow or a handkerchief belonging to Paul was enough to bring healing (Acts 5:12-16; 19:11-12). How wonderful! Why wasn't I born back then?!

But—was *everybody* healed during those remarkable days of establishing the Church? Did anyone go away wondering why God chose to heal so many others—but not them?

Paul. My mind's eye follows him along his laborious ministry years. How dynamically God chose to work through this yielded man! However, the great apostle spent his life suffering with what he called his "infirmity" and "thorn in the flesh" (II Corinthians 12:5-7). With so many deliverances and extraordinary miracles going on around him—yes, even being worked *through* him—surely at first Paul expected that mighty touch of God in his own need. "I besought the Lord thrice," he wrote, "that [the thorn] might depart from me" (verse 8). But it didn't.

In II Corinthians 12:9 we read that the only answer God gave to Paul's request for healing was, "My grace is sufficient for thee: for my strength is made perfect in weakness." Paul accepted that, realizing that without his infirmity men might be tempted to exalt him above measure due to "the abundance of the revelations" given him. Humbly accepting his lack of healing, Paul wrote, "Most gladly therefore will I rather glory in my infirmities, that the power of Christ may rest upon me" (verse 9). And the power of Christ certainly did rest upon Paul, using him in a mighty way to spread the Gospel—despite the thorn.

And yet... While I know, of course, that God had a good reason, it's a bit difficult to imagine why He would allow that thorn. Yes, it was key in keeping Paul humble, but Peter and John had an "abundance of revelations" too, and they didn't get a thorn. Why?

We are not told.

Do you ever face those unanswered "whys"? Why did your sister's courtship turn out so beautifully, progressing into a happy marriage, while yours fell apart and left you wounded and alone? Why are most people blessed with strong bodies, while you suffer daily from a progressive illness? Why are many women given charming personalities and physical beauty, while you feel shy and homely? Why was your niece born with Down's syndrome, while so many other children are healthy? Why are you—a woman who dearly

loves children and homemaking—kept in singlehood, working with *other women's* neglected children? Why must you struggle alone to support yourself, when you would love to be a keeper at home with a husband to provide? Why does God's Word say, "I will therefore that the younger women marry, bear children, [and] guide the house" (I Timothy 5:14), and yet He hasn't allowed you to do that? With so many blessings being granted to those around you, why doesn't God bless *you* in those ways too?

Unanswered. Except in the way Paul was answered. Do you hear your Savior speaking? "My precious daughter, purchased with My blood! My grace is sufficient for you; My strength is made perfect in weakness."

Yes, to our finite minds the questions may remain. They surge up within us, only to meet the inexplicable "Trust Me." But what peace and acceptance fill us when we realize *who* it is that speaks those words! Stop a minute—what is that you see? The form of One beloved on a cruel Roman cross! The Friend closer than a brother, the mighty God, everlasting Father, King of kings: wounded and bruised—for you! Contemplate the magnitude of such love, and, like Paul, glory in the "infirmities" this love allows, letting God's grace and strength suffice. Then watch all your questions fade away in the tide of such love—even if they remain "unanswered."

I Trust His Love

My life is in God's hands—
He never fails; His plan
For me is good, and He
Performs it perfectly.
I TRUST HIS LOVE.

So forward I will go—
And fear not, for I know
He will not let me stray;
He'll shelter me each day.
I TRUST HIS LOVE.

> "O Lord! my best desires fulfill.
> AND HELP ME TO RESIGN
> Life, health, and comfort to Thy will,
> And make Thy pleasure mine."
> —*William Cowper*

> "*Ill that He blesses is our good,*
> AND UNBLEST GOOD IS ILL;
> And all is right that seems most wrong,
> If it be His sweet will."
> —*F.W. Faber*

"And we know that all things *work together for good* to them that love God, to them who are the called according to his purpose."

—*Romans 8:28*

"How reasonable it is to trust ourselves to the

KEEPING OF INFINITE LOVE,

and infinite wisdom, and infinite power!"

—*Thomas Erskine*

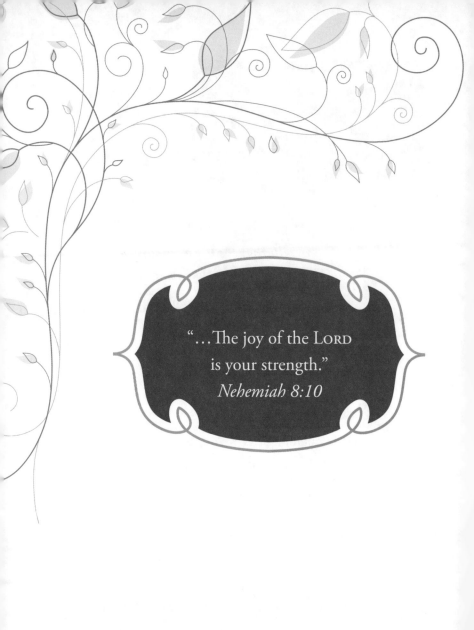

"…The joy of the LORD
is your strength."
Nehemiah 8:10

…Ordered Steps…

9

The Choice

The alarm clock on my nightstand screeches out a rude awakening. My blurry eyes open to meet another day.

·*Another day older*
·*Another day single*
·*Another day doing work that wouldn't be my first choice*
·*Another day of monotonous sameness*
·*Another day of meeting **The Choice***

The Choice? Yes, it greets me the moment I awake. I can allow clouds of self-pity to dim my spirit for the rest of the day, or choose to throw back the curtains and let the joy of God shine in.

The Self-Pity Choice

·Another day older—life is short and it's passing me by! I'm missing out on so much that most people my age take for granted. And each day adds to the reality that my youth is quickly fading. Before I know it, I'll be old. No wonder I'm discouraged!

·Another day single—yes, alone! No special one to talk to, share with, or work beside in his endeavors! No one to fill my voids, care especially for me, or meet my needs. No wonder I'm discouraged!

·Another day doing work that wouldn't be my first choice—yes, doing a job that doesn't even *resemble* my dreams of being a contented homemaker! No wonder I'm discouraged!

·Another day of monotonous sameness—no thrilling events, no exciting expectations, no grand mountains to climb, no adventures to meet. Just the dull mundane. No wonder I'm discouraged!

·Another day of meeting The Choice—yes, whether or not I will collapse under such dullness or toil wearily on. No wonder I'm discouraged!

Or Choosing to Accept God's Will

·Another day older—yes, isn't God good?! He has given me one more day to walk through, hand-in-hand with Him! To enjoy the beauty of His creation—a tiny wildflower, a patch of blue sky peeking through the clouds, the chorus of tree frogs in the aspen grove. Another day to say a cheering word, touch a needy heart, point a wanderer toward Home. Another day to tell my loved ones, "I love you!" Another day to rejoice and be glad in. No wonder I'm joyful!

·Another day single—yes, single-heartedly pressing toward God. Working with Him in His endeavors, thriving in fellowship with Him, dwelling on His Word, communing with Him through prayer. Another day in which He fills the void of what He withholds, and gives sufficient grace for needs that, for a single, must remain unmet. Another day looking only to God. No wonder I'm joyful!

·Another day doing work that wouldn't be my first choice—yes, but since *God* has placed me here, I can find strength that as *His choice*, it's the best place to be until He leads elsewhere! Therefore the work becomes hallowed and special as I seek to do it as unto Him who gave His very life for me. No wonder I'm joyful!

·Another day of monotonous sameness—yes, it may appear so at first glance, but it is *not* so! No day is a carbon-copy. If I keep my eyes open, I can find new evidences of God's goodness in seemingly trivial events; I can discover small avenues of service that strengthen and encourage those around me; I can be surprised by little joys that—if I take notice of them!—will uplift me along the way. No wonder I'm joyful!

·Another day of meeting The Choice—yes, the deciding factor in which I choose either *my* will, and wallow in self-pity because things aren't just as I'd like them to be; or *God's* will, and glory in the fact that He orders my steps and does all things well.

"Father, today I choose to be joyful!"

New Morning

Morning light infused the room,
Dispelling all the dark and gloom.
Praise God! Praise God! The morning's here
With mercies new, and hope, and cheer!

The battles of my yesterday
Have with the dark night passed away.
O Lord, all praise and thanks to You
For making each day bright and new!

...Ordered Steps...

"One thing is indisputable: the chronic mood of looking longingly at what we have not, or thankfully at what we have, realizes *two very different types of character*. And we certainly can encourage the one or the other."

–*L.C. Smith*

"Seek to cultivate a buoyant, *joyous sense* of the crowded kindnesses of God in your daily life."
–*Alexander MacLaren*

"The surest method of arriving at a KNOWLEDGE OF GOD'S ETERNAL PURPOSES about us is to be found in the right use of the present moment."
–*F.W. Faber*

"WHATEVER HAPPENS TO ME EACH DAY IS MY DAILY BREAD, provided I do not refuse to take it from Thy hand, and feed upon it."

–*Fénelon*

"He hath made everything
beautiful in his time."
Ecclesiastes 3:11

...Ordered Steps...

10

God Sent the Rain!

It is midsummer and, wiping out all memory of the rugged winters we have, a suffocating heat wave hovers over our community. The hot sun beats relentlessly on a parched and dusty earth. Adding to my already withered spirits, it saps my strength and leaves me immobile and lethargic.

I pray for rain. Puffy white clouds silently cover the scorching blue, only to add humidity to the already breathless heat. Then they dissipate without a drop of rain. For days this has happened. I've nearly lost hope. How discouraging to see the vegetable and flower gardens shrivel before my eyes! It seems like a fitting analogy of my life.

How weary—unutterably weary—and shriveled I feel! Tears sting my eyes as I look at my prayer list. Beside many petitions are scribbled dates and brief notes about how God has answered. But this one critical request, added more than two years ago, remains unanswered. I face the same void as before—with no hope in sight.

God knows the need. To ask for its fulfillment is in accordance to His Word. Little clouds of hope show up on my horizon, only to evaporate and leave me disappointed. I shrivel in the heat of the trial. Will God never answer?

It's a breathless night now, and I'm falling asleep with the brightness of the moon spilling over a dry landscape outside. I'm too hot and wilted to even pray for rain. But what is this? As I sleep fitfully, the clouds come silently to veil the moon. The limp curtains flutter gently. In the wee hours of the morning I am awakened by a steady beating on the roof. A cooling breeze, laden with the fragrance of rain, sweeps in the open window. Wide awake now, my heart rejoices in awe. I had given up on asking, yet quietly and unexpectedly God sent the rain—anyway. Suddenly I realize that He had this planned from the beginning. He sent it in His time. And now the glory is His alone.

It's early dawn and I climb out of bed and take up my prayer journal. The same old request meets me, but this time I find myself smiling quietly. God knows the need—He has the answer planned. In His time and way, it will come. And the glory will be His alone! The unexpected rain is still pattering on the roof—I had been worried that it would never come, but God hadn't been.

Weary, killing heat—then glorious rain! "Lord, are the waiting times sent so that we will fully recognize the fact that You alone are our Provider? Oh, deliver me from my weary discouragement! Renew my faith to anticipate Your time and way.

"Thank You, Lord, for this lesson so beautifully illustrated in the fresh, balmy breeze and the clean, lovely world washed by rain. Truly, 'They that wait upon the Lord shall renew their strength' (Isaiah 40:31). My strength is renewed. Amen."

"When it seemed impossible that help could come, help did come, for God has His own resources. He is not confined. In ten thousand different ways and at ten thousand different times God may help us."
–*George Mueller*

...Ordered Steps...

God's Time

There is a time—
A season set—
A purpose under heaven,
For all the things
The Father plans:
Fear not, they will be given.

And He hath made
Each thing He planned
Beautiful in His own time.
Obscured from view,
Nonetheless true;
Await His grand design!

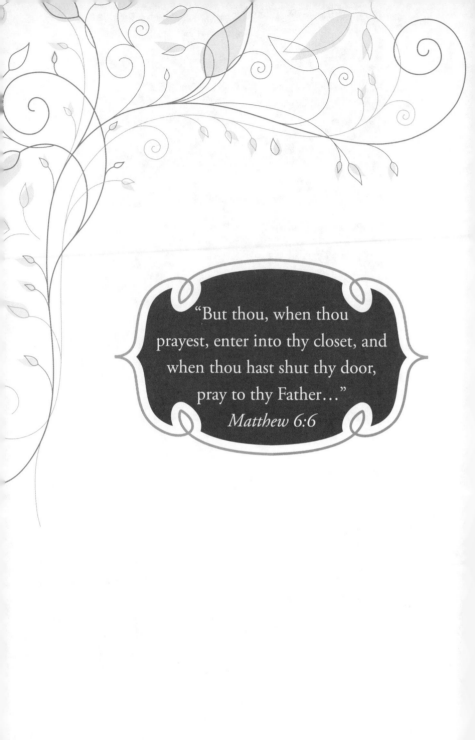

"But thou, when thou prayest, enter into thy closet, and when thou hast shut thy door, pray to thy Father…"

Matthew 6:6

…Ordered Steps…

11

The Vital Connection

The sun hasn't yet peeked above the horizon. As I open my curtains I see the pre-glow in the east. Groggily I reach for my Bible and prayer journal, trying to keep awake as I crawl into my daily prayer time.

The seconds drag. I yawn and glance at the clock—again. Sigh of relief! The 45 minutes I set aside for prayer time is over for another day. Now I can get to the *really* important things on my to-do list!

Have you ever found yourself there?

For many years I heard—with a jealous twinge—about Christians who treasured their prayer time. They testified of sweet communion with God, strengthened spiritual power, and answers to requests on a daily basis. Sure, I had encountered such experiences myself, but for me they came few and far between.

Often I wondered if vital prayer was only for a "privileged few"—

like George Mueller of Bristol, Ole Hallesby, or R.A. Torrey. Maybe the average Christian was expected to plod along through boring and perfunctory prayers, finding only occasional times of true communion.

But the prospect of spending my entire life waking up to yet another futile prayer session was discouraging.

I remember when I embarked on the quest for rejuvenating my prayer life—I just could *not* go on in the same rut any longer. If vital prayer was—as I had been told—the right, privilege, and duty of all Christians, then I determined to discover it in my daily life. The lesson has taken time—and is ongoing! But here are some of the things I am learning.

1. Contemplate What Prayer Is

Remember the statement, "Prayer is the vital connection between God and man"? Think how true that is! It's astonishing to realize that prayer is conversation with the *Almighty God!* It is by prayer that we first came to Him in the name of Christ, with confession and belief unto salvation. Prayer is how we build a personal relationship with God. It is the avenue by which we engage in spiritual battle. Through prayer we bring down blessings from heaven. Prayer helps to break strongholds. And prayer keeps us spiritually alive.

"Prayer," wrote a grand old writer, "is the breath of the soul." Without breath, we die.

2. Remember Who Is Listening When You Pray!

Coming to my prayer time, I have often felt like a child with a toy telephone—a lot of talking on one side, and only thin air on the other. Is there *really* Someone listening when I pray?

But the truth is staggering in its wonder. In prayer, we are actually talking with the Creator of all things! And He assures us it isn't one-sided: "…While [you] are yet speaking, I will hear" (Isaiah 65:24).

When I stop to realize who it is that I'm coming to, it evokes an attitude of awe, gratitude, and excitement that I—a finite, faulty human being—may, through Christ, come with humble boldness into the throne room of God (see Hebrews 4:16). Stop and consider the wonder of that! When we enter our prayer closet, we have the privilege of praying *not* to a stranger or a cold, distant Being, but to *our heavenly Father who loves us!* (See Matthew 6:6.) There isn't merely thin air on the "other side." We are conversing with the Almighty God, Redeemer, and Comforter; the One who plans our days, and guards, guides, and gives abundantly (see Jeremiah 29:11; I Samuel 2:9; Isaiah 58:11; Romans 8:32).

Acknowledging these truths has helped to make my prayer time precious and fulfilling.

3. Have Faith in God!

What are the attributes of God? He is just, merciful, good, immutable, faithful, and more! We need to search out all of His attributes and let them increase our faith. C.H. Spurgeon, in his beautiful commentary on the Psalms, *The Treasury of David*, wrote: "Rightly viewed, all the perfections of Deity become pleas for faith." How true!

When we have faith in who God is, we cease to doubt and question. We find Him to be great enough and true enough to trust in—even if we can't understand His dealings.

By this, we will learn to trust the unknown to the One who knows. Trust His promises. Trust that He meant what He said when He proclaimed, "I said not unto the seed of Jacob, Seek ye me in vain: I the LORD speak righteousness, I declare things that are right" (Isaiah 45:19).

4. Combine Bible Study with Prayer

True communion is two-sided. To hear from God, we need His Word open before us. In this way we can "try the spirits" (see I John 4:1), holding up to the light of infallible Truth whatever enters our consciousness. By meditating on God's Word during prayer, we can search out His will, contemplate His promises, and discover His plans for us. Reading His "Letter" to us, we learn His heart.

5. Prepare!

It would seem audacious to request an audience with an earthly leader, such as the President of the United States, and then to arrive at the granted appointment disinterested and totally unprepared. Yet day after day, Christians (like myself!) come before the Sovereign Ruler of all with a sluggish, preoccupied attempt at conversation.

I have found it helpful to spend time bringing myself into focus before jumping into prayer. Reading Scripture that pertains to current events in my life; singing a hymn that suits the need and draws my spirit to adoration and surrender; sorting through my prayer journal and highlighting new reasons for confession, praise, intercession, and petition. This brings me up to date, so that my prayers are purposeful—not mere repetition. All of this only takes a few minutes, yet it makes all the difference!

6. Be Honest—God Knows the Truth Already!

In human conversation, we tend to put our best foot forward. In prayer, there is no need for pretense. Why attempt to cover the state of our hearts before the One who knows us better than we know ourselves? We can come to God with complete honesty about everything! He is full of compassion; He knows our frame of dust (see Psalm 103:14), and He is ready and willing to forgive and renew.

7. Don't Let Prayer Replace Action

Sometimes we wonder why we are not seeing answers to certain prayers. In my life I've found that, on occasion, I tend to simply pray, when God wants me to pray *and* do.

Reading Exodus 14:10-18—the account of the children of Israel up against the Red Sea—has helped me to see the significance of this. Let's take a look at it:

Up against the Red Sea and pursued by the Egyptian army, the children of Israel "cried out unto the Lord" in fear.

When no answer came, bitter complaints rose up. Moses, in an attempt to soothe and hearten them, said, "Fear ye not, stand still, and see the salvation of the Lord, which he will shew to you to day. …The Lord shall fight for you."

Sounds good, doesn't it? But we read further that God reprimanded Moses. "Wherefore criest thou unto me?" He asked. "Speak unto the children of Israel, that they go forward." He had already promised to deliver them from the Egyptians; He expected them to fearlessly move ahead in trust.

What was the result when they finally did? When they took that step forward, it moved God to do what their cries and prayers had not—He parted the sea and led them through unharmed. Their enemies, in hot pursuit, died as the waters closed over them.

Yes, there are times when we should stand still and wait (see Psalm 62:1,5). But when God has revealed to us in His Word what He expects, it is fear and timidity that keeps us from the very step that will bring down power and deliverance. Let us go forward!

8. Leave It with God

There is tremendous relief in casting, or "rolling" (as the original has it), our burdens on God. The *Amplified Bible* renders Psalm 55:22

in this way: "Cast your burden on the Lord [releasing the weight of it] and He will sustain you; He will never allow the [consistently] righteous to be moved (made to slip, fall, or fail)."

I love the oft-quoted words of Robert Leighton: "Roll thy cares, and thyself with them, as one burden, all on thy God." There is no need to take back a burden once committed to God. If we roll our very selves onto Him, we may rest in His power and love. He will take care of us!

9. Expect Answers!

Don't be lethargic about unanswered prayer. Our God is the God who said, "Call unto me, and I will answer thee, and shew thee great and mighty things, which thou knowest not" (Jeremiah 33:3). And Jesus said, "And whatsoever ye shall ask in my name, that will I do, that the Father may be glorified in the Son. If ye shall ask any thing in my name, I will do it. If ye love me, keep my commandments" (John 14:13-15). Though answers may take time, don't have the poetic, misty, "sometime, somewhere" view of their fulfillment. The fullness of the answer may not be instantaneous, but the moment we pray the answer process begins. If it takes time, don't give up. Wait for it; it will come (see Habakkuk 2:3). Our prayers are not requests "standing in line" for attention. They are already answered; the time of their fulfillment is set (see Genesis 21:2), and we can look forward in eagerness.

God's answers to our prayers may not always be what we expect. Remember Paul's request to be delivered from his "thorn" (II Corinthians 12)? But we can rest in this fact: God is all-wise; His answers are for our absolute best, bringing us the greatest joy and fulfillment possible. We may go forward fearlessly to meet our answers—the One who loves our souls has prepared them for us!

...Ordered Steps...

· · · · · · · · · · · · · · · ·

It's prayer time again! The glow of daybreak lightens the sky. I take up my Bible and prayer journal, wide awake. I have an engagement with the Ruler of heaven and earth—it will be a blessed experience! The minutes pass quickly. Has it already been an hour? But that's okay. Other things can wait. This is the most important event on my to-do list.

Rejuvenating your prayer life. Yes, it can be done! God has replaced my once-dead prayers with satisfying, precious, and living communion. If He could do it for me, He can do the same for you!

Assured

You hear my groanings and my cry;
My tears are kept by You.
And interceding at each sigh,
The Spirit helps me, too.

You ever live to plead for me—
I will not be dismayed.
You work all things out perfectly—
I will not be afraid.

I will not fear,
I will not fear.
The God who lives for me can hear,
And He will answer as I pray,
And He will work in His best way.
The God who lives for me can hear—
I will not fear.
I will not fear.

...Ordered Steps...

"Would the believer, therefore, have his faith strengthened, he must especially *give time to God,* who tries his faith in order to prove to His child, in the end, how willing He is to help and deliver him, the moment it is good for him."

–George Mueller, Answers to Prayer, page 37

"Prayer should be the means by which I, at all times, receive all that I need, and for this reason, be my daily refuge, my daily consolation, my daily joy."

–Ole Hallesby, Prayer, page 38

"THERE IS NO GREATER JOY on earth or in heaven than communion with God, and prayer in the name of Jesus brings us into communion with Him. The Psalmist was surely not speaking only of future blessedness, but also of present blessedness when he said, *'In thy presence is fullness of joy' (Psalm 16:11).* Oh, the unutterable joy of those moments when in our prayers we really press into the presence of God!"

–R.A. Torry, How to Pray, page 16

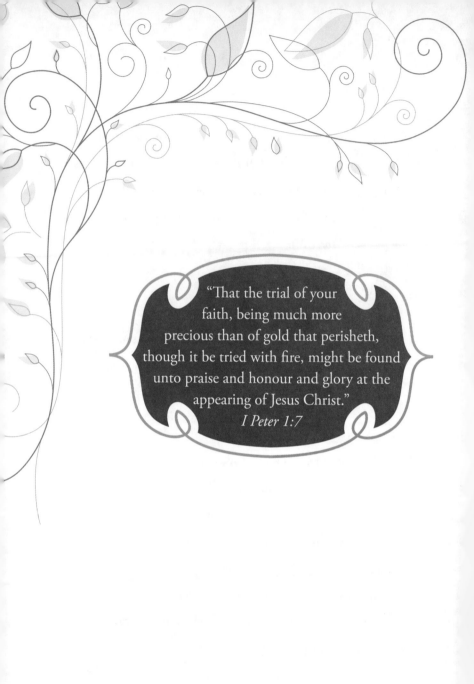

"That the trial of your
faith, being much more
precious than of gold that perisheth,
though it be tried with fire, might be found
unto praise and honour and glory at the
appearing of Jesus Christ."
I Peter 1:7

12

Sometimes the fire Hurts
(Thoughts after a wedding announcement)

"Dear Lord, the past few months have been such blessed peace. Contentment has permeated my heart, obscuring those old longings and dreams. I've been so busy with my job, ministry, and home duties. Life has been good, and I was feeling that I had finally come to the place where I could sincerely say, 'I adore Your will for me, all-perfect Lord!'

"Then, today.

"Ah, You know. You knew even before I opened the mailbox and took out that glossy white envelope that held the news. My childhood friend, one who has been such a help and encouragement to me along life's way, is soon to marry a godly man and begin the journey we used to dream about! And I? Once again the one who's left alone.

"Father! It hurts! I feel like my heart, all unsuspecting, received a wounding blow. Oh no, it isn't that I grudge my friend this joy. It isn't that I wish she were *not* stepping into a marriage so clearly planned by You. It is just this: that *I am not.* That's where the blow comes, Father. Why is it that You do not seem to have a special man for me?

"Caught off guard today, all of those longings and dreams wash over me again in a battering flood. Father, didn't You say that it is *not* good for men to be alone—which assumes it isn't good for women, either? And didn't You design marriage, calling it good? Don't You care that I feel I can't bear the single path another step? Have You forsaken and forgotten me? Oh God, You who plan my life—why are You doing this to me? Do You even care? I thought I was over such searing questions, but tonight I discover I am not.

"But what is this You are saying? Your Spirit draws me to Your Word. I search the pages, seeking an answer. Yes, now I remember. You sit as a refiner and purifier, to purge me of impurities as gold and silver are refined (Job 23:10; Zechariah 13:9; Malachi 3:2-3; etc.). You test my faith (I Peter 1:7). The process involves fire to burn away the dross—the sin, the pride, the self-will. It is Your right to choose the flaming trials for each of Your children. This happens to be the one You've chosen for me. But the fires will never destroy me. Their purpose is to purify.

"I close my eyes and hear Your still, small voice."

"Daughter, I sit over you as a refiner—yet how much more precious than gold is your faith to Me! My purpose is to see in you a pure reflection of Myself, therefore I must remove the dross. It is because I love you that I turn up the heat. Why, My child, are you surprised that sometimes the fire will hurt?"

Suddenly my tears flow freely. "Father, I am sorry that I questioned Your wisdom. Now I remember the core of all my purpose and reason to be! It is neither marriage nor singlehood that I should focus on.

...Ordered Steps...

Only this: being in Your will for me today.

"I am praying again, Lord, a petition for myself. This time so different! It is this, that You will keep me in Your will all through life—each day!—and draw me closer no matter the cost, and bring me safely Home. That's all that really matters. Thank You for hearing and answering my prayer; for caring enough to send only what is best for me.

"I think of all the things I want in life—sometimes the pain is so deep and the desire strong. Ah! So *this* is how the fire feels! But even without one of my desires ever met—even if this flame will never cease on earth—I can still be glad and rejoice in *You*, for You are my portion now and forever. *You* are all that I really need this night, and through eternity.

"Lord Father, I give myself to You again. Do with me as You will. I am Yours. Even though sometimes the fire hurts, I choose to trust You tonight. Amen."

Restore My Soul

Why the sorrow, why the pain, dear Lord?
It seems as if the way is just too hard.
It seems as if You do not hear me pray—
And all my skies are gray.

Why is it that You let my heart be torn?
(Sometimes I wish that I were never born!
Sometimes I think I'm sobbing drops of blood
And sinking in the flood.)

As a refiner over untouched ore,
Seeking precious metal from the core,
You stoke the fire to a purging light—
I feel the flame tonight.

And yet You hold me in Your mighty hand.
And yet You promise that You have a plan.
And yet Your love for me covers the whole—
And so restores my soul.

...Ordered Steps...

"For I reckon that the sufferings of this present time
ARE NOT WORTHY to be compared
with the glory which shall be revealed in us."
—Romans 8:18

"There is a set time for
putting into the furnace,
and a set time for taking
out of the furnace."

—Selected

"He healeth the broken in heart,
and bindeth up their wounds."
—Psalm 147:3

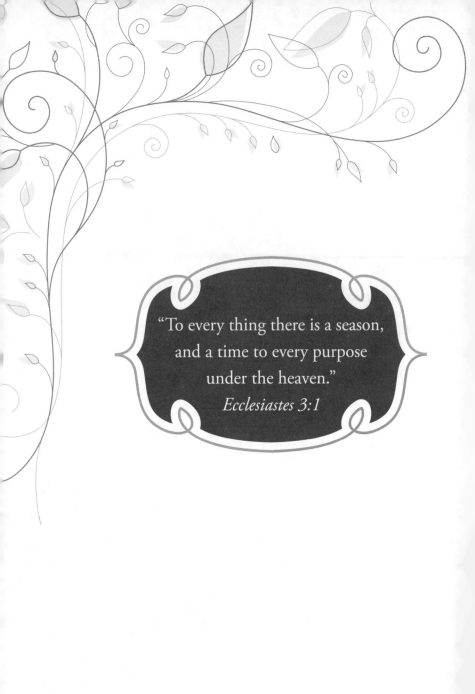

"To every thing there is a season, and a time to every purpose under the heaven."

Ecclesiastes 3:1

...Ordered Steps...

13

The Thaw

It was the winter of 2007-2008, the one we still call "The Big Winter." For weeks the mercury in our thermometer huddled well below 0°. Still and cold, the very air seemed frozen in place. Clouds hung thickly, obscuring the mountain ranges that were draped in white. Pines bent low beneath heavy snow, while a steady veil of small white flakes cascaded silently into a swiftly deepening expanse.

Just when the clouds would begin to break, a new storm crept in on the heels of the preceding one. Men layered on extreme weather gear and manned snowplows, shovels, and tractors in a constant battle against the seemingly endless whirl of white that covered streets, clogged driveways, and burdened roofs.

Ice fishermen lamented the four feet of snow that made breaking a trail on the iced-over lakes a backbreaking excursion. Snowmobiles stayed inert under tarps, as drifts made driving nearly impossible. Adventurous skiers were turned away at the mountain pass due to massive avalanches. Road crews worked around the clock clearing roads, only to have them drifted shut again in a matter of hours.

Snow, snow, snow! Would it ever end? Held prisoner behind frosted windowpanes, I longed for release from the frozen landscape. I dreamed of warm spring weather—weather that didn't require putting on four layers of clothing before venturing out-of-doors, only to sink waist-deep in crunchy-cold, powdery snow. I dreamed of breaks in the thick clouds, of balmy air, of warm fingers of sunlight reaching through to unlock the chains of cold. Yet looking out over that icy-white world, God's promise of spring seemed nearly impossible.

The long winter held on well into March, obscuring everything behind seven-foot-tall mounds of snow. Desperate workers hauled dump truck loads to the rivers, dumping them in the only available space that wasn't entirely snowbound.

The situation seemed to be reaching a climax of misery. Then, suddenly, the icy grip loosened. Overnight, the air lost its pinching, lung-burning cold. Clouds broke into scuttling lumps of gray-white, letting in snatches of beautiful, warming sunlight. The mercury crawled up to an amazing 30°. Snow on the roofs began melting to form long fingers of icicles across the eaves. One day soon after, as I strapped chains on my boots and headed out into the fickle sunshine, I followed icy snowplow tracks down our road and found a place where the snow had been worn through to a patch of—mud!!! Oh, joy! The elation of seeing anything other than solid-packed snow was wonderful!

By late March the road was nearly clear of snow. I could squish and squash along in old tennis shoes, marveling at the beauty of

...Ordered Steps...

balmy air that carried the fragrance of wet earth and the sound of birdsong. Squirrels frisked in the pines that now stood straight and tall, released from their weight of snow. Tiny shoots of green peeked out of the slush, and the peaceful sound of melting snow seeping into the earth brought hope that soon the white mounds would disappear. Taking deep breaths of the invigorating breeze, I looked up at the sun peeking from behind stubborn clouds, and smiled. God *was* good and faithful. As impossible as it had seemed, spring *had* come as He had promised. Yes, "The Big Winter" was past!

Truly the seasons are illustrative of what we face inside. Sometimes we are in the cold grip of a winter season in our spirits. Our circumstances look like mountains of snow, closing us in. Our prayers appear to be frozen in the air, never penetrating the trouble-clouded sky. God seems far away and we feel so weak and cold. It looks impossible that the clouds of this trial will ever break; that the warming sunshine of healing, hope, joy, and peace will ever shine through.

But we need not be afraid. God is the God of seasons, orderly and certain. As surely as the thaw came that long-awaited spring, so the thaw will come in our cold spirits, bringing shining joy, soothing peace, warming hope, and fresh spiritual newness.

Winter does not last forever! We must never despair, but instead keep our eyes open for that first ray of sunshine warming our spirits to life; that little patch of good soil as a sign of hope; that first blade of grass as a promise of new life where we thought all was dead.

"What an enjoyment it is to walk abroad after illness," C.H. Spurgeon wrote, "and what a delight to be strong in the Lord after a season of prostration! 'And I will strengthen them in the Lord: and they shall walk up and down in his name, saith the Lord'

(Zechariah 10:12)." This can be our lifeline through the weary season. God promises to strengthen us; to thaw our frozen hearts until they can cause us to walk joyfully in the name of our Lord.

Considering the stability of seasons in nature, we may confidently thank God and take courage. The thaw *will* come in our own hearts too. Hang on a little longer—it just might come today!

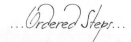

Change Will Come

Fast frozen by the touch of cold
Frosty breath, and in the hold
Of the most unfriendly hand
Of winter-land.

But came the warming touch of spring!
Isn't it a wondrous thing
How its finger quick unwound
What held me bound?

The lesson of the melting snow:
Change will come—God made it so.
Orderly, the seasons move
Faithful to prove

The goodness of God's perfect care
In nature, and my life. There
Comes the touch of His strong hand
As He has planned.

"...O LORD, thou art
our father; we are the clay, and
thou our potter; and we all are
the work of thy hand."

Isaiah 64:8

...Ordered Steps...

14

All to Jesus

"**O**h, good—that's one of my favorites!" I tell myself as the song leader opens the service with the tender and lovely words of "I Surrender All." I join in readily.

"All to Jesus I surrender,

All to Him I freely give—"

Hmm. What is the definition of "all" anyway? "The total entity or extent of; the whole number, amount, or quantity of; each and every thing."

Does that include the nagging pinprick fears about my future?

The inner discouragements over my age and how fleeting youth is?

My sometimes-discontentment with being single?

My hopes and dreams, ministry and talents?

My joys and treasures, interests and occupation?

My concerns about what others may think of me when I follow

where God calls—and it's not where some believe I should be?

My "right" to plan and choose my own future?

Yes. All means *all*. Dismay rises in my heart. "You mean surrender each and every thing? Freely give up the total extent of it all and let go? No longer be an individual with my own desires and interests?"

In my mind's eye is the vision of every part of my life being released into a gigantic dark void called "surrender." Suddenly I'm left with a vast emptiness, my hands hanging limply at my sides, no purpose or ambition to urge me forward. Just a lump of unshaped clay! What a horrible thought. Tears flood my eyes. "Is this what You *really* want me to do, Lord?"

Then the words penetrate my consciousness. Peace washes over my agitated heart. Ah, it is not simply, "I surrender all," but, "All to Jesus I surrender." Doesn't that make every bit of difference in the world?!

Jesus! I go over His titles as though I'm counting my treasures. My Advocate (I John 2:1), the Almighty (Revelation 1:8), Alpha and Omega (Revelation 1:8), blessed and only Potentate (I Timothy 6:15), Chief Shepherd (I Peter 5:4), Christ of God (Luke 9:20), Counselor (Isaiah 9:6), Creator (John 1:3), Deliverer (Romans 11:26), Everlasting Father (Isaiah 9:6), Great High Priest (Hebrews 4:14), Savior (Luke 2:11), Mighty God (Isaiah 9:6)—and so much more! How wonderful! In His Word I hear Him call me to Himself and say, "Child, cast your anxious care on Me—I care for you!" (see I Peter 5:7); "Give your all to Me, I have good plans for you!" (Jeremiah 29:11). And suddenly a whole new view of surrender meets my eye!

I smile with joy. To give up every part of my life to my wonderful Lord is not releasing everything into an empty void, never again to experience hope, interest, fulfillment, and purpose. Instead, it is giving it all into almighty hands and competent care! It is acknowledging the right my Lord has over my life, choosing to bow to that right, and expectantly trusting everything to His all-knowing wisdom, most tender love, and perfect faithfulness. It is making an exchange for less of me and more of Him!

Now I begin to see that to hang on to my all is like letting a two-year-old play with potter's clay. I would squish it into a worthless mess! But to give up my all to Jesus is like letting the Master Potter shape and form with utmost skill.

So *this* is what He plans to do: to take my fragile vessel and infuse me with His power! To take my daily life and make of it something of eternal value! To give and take away as He sees fit! Only when I've surrendered my all to Him can He shower me with these blessings. I lift up my head and join in the song once more:

"All to Jesus I surrender,
Lord, I give myself to Thee;
Fill me with Thy love and power,
Let Thy blessings fall on me."

My All

Great Savior of my own eternal soul, I know
That this, my ransomed life, to Thee alone I owe.
And coming to Thy blessed feet, once pierced for me,
I give my all—*my all*—beloved Lord, to Thee.

...Ordered Steps...

Entire

ALL THINE!

The thoughts, the hopes, the dreams,
The inner, outer things,
The plans for future days,
The heart that sings Thy praise.

ALL THINE!

The fears, the doubts, the pain,
The sorrows and the shame,
The broken, contrite heart,
The songless lips, the dark.

ALL THINE!

Dear Lord, I yield to Thee
Each minute part of me,
Each sigh, each song, each tear,
Each hidden corner here.

ALL THINE!

To take, to shape and form,
To mold by trial or storm;
To fashion me anew
In likeness, Lord, of You.

"Be kindly affectioned one to another with brotherly love; in honour preferring one another."
Romans 12:10

15

Do Something Kind

Gloom. It looms on my horizon when I least expect it. It hits when the weather is bad, I've got a cold, or there are dishes to wash when I'd rather do something else! Gloom emerges when special plans fall through, my schedule goes haywire, I get junk mail when I'd expected a letter from a friend, or I find I'm out of molasses—*after* I already mixed most of the gingerbread ingredients!

But gloom can also shadow my life in deeper ways. I'm not recuperating from an injury as fast as I'd hoped, my paycheck isn't going to cover all my needs, another birthday rolls around and I'm *still* single, somebody makes a cutting remark about my most-disliked physical feature, or someone *else* is asked to teach the Sunday school class that *I* wanted! No wonder I've got a frown on my face. Life just doesn't seem to be treating me right! Suddenly the sky is very black.

Notice something interesting about those paragraphs? All of the

"I's" and "me's"! It seems like a lot of gloom comes from being a bit too focused on one person—that woman in the mirror.

Can there possibly be a way to escape those familiar clouds of despondency? "When you find yourself, as I dare say you sometimes do, overpowered as it were by melancholy," wrote the Rev. John Keble in the early 1800s, "the best way is to go out, and do something kind to somebody or other."

The suggestion arrests my attention. What?! Turn the magnifying glass off of my own discouragement and hurts, and take a look at *other people's* needs?

Good advice! And guess what! The Rev. John Keble didn't come up with that idea all by himself!

·"Be ye kind one to another" (Ephesians 4:32).

·"Be kindly affectioned one to another with brotherly love; in honour preferring one another" (Romans 12:10).

·"To do good and to communicate forget not: for with such sacrifices God is well pleased" (Hebrews 13:16).

·"Blessed is he that considereth the poor" (Psalm 41:1).

·"Love as brethren, be pitiful, be courteous" (I Peter 3:8).

·"Comfort the feebleminded, support the weak, be patient toward all men" (I Thessalonians 5:14).

·"As we have therefore opportunity, let us do good unto all men, especially unto them who are of the household of faith" (Galatians 6:10).

Suddenly my mind is very occupied—and not with myself! There's a teenage girl I know who is struggling with doubt and fear—why not spend some time with her, sharing how the Lord helped me through a similar experience? Grandma mentioned that she gets lonely living so far from most of her family—wouldn't a homemade card brighten her day? There's a family struggling to put food on the table since the father lost his job—a dozen cookies and a loaf of bread would probably be cheering. The cashier at the grocery store looks exhausted—why not take time to share a smile and a sincere "thanks for your help!"? That busy friend with five little ones has more dirty dishes than I ever do—I'll stop by and lend a hand! Suddenly the sky is very blue.

Does gloom stalk you like it sometimes does me? When clouds gather and waves of melancholy try to drag you under, reach for this buoyant motto: "Do something kind!" It will help to keep you from sinking in self-pity—I know, because I've tested it! And I'm trying to make it my new way of life.

Of course, ever since starting out on this new way, I haven't had a whole lot of time for focusing on that woman in the mirror—but I'll let you in on a secret: when I last caught a glimpse of her, she was smiling.

for You

I Thessalonians 5:23-24

I think of you, and turn my mind to prayer;
I lift you up to God, present you there
As one dear to my heart, and so I pray
For God's surrounding care for you today.

May He preserve your spirit, body, soul
As blameless unto Christ, a perfect whole;
And sanctify you then in ev'ry way;
And bring you safely through each passing day.

...Ordered Steps...

"To cultivate kindness is a great part of the business of life."
—Samuel Johnson

How To Chase Out Gloom

When gloom casts shadows on my life,
Where does the sunshine hide?
It's just behind the shades called "me",
The curtains "self" and "pride."
But when I throw them back, I find
The feelings that annoy
Will scatter swiftly in the light
Of bringing others joy!

"Let our life be one of self-sacrifice, **ALWAYS**

STUDYING THE WELFARE OF OTHERS,

finding our highest joy in blessing others."

—Andrew Murray

"For I the Lord thy God will hold thy right hand, saying unto thee, Fear not; I will help thee."

Isaiah 41:13

...Ordered Steps...

16

Someone to Walk With

The sun was shining and the air was crisp and fresh. What better time for a walk! I zipped on my snow boots and layered on a thick scarf, cozy sweater, and warm coat. Outside, winter sunlight danced on snow that squeaked under my feet. Pine trees stood out vivid green against gnarled gray branches of bare Gambel oak. Snowcapped mountains peeked through clearings in the forest. Such a beautiful day!

As I crunched through the snow, I became aware of a dark feeling clouding the radiant beauty around me. Little darts needled into my contentment. Sure, it was a perfect day for a walk, but once again here I was—*alone*.

For some reason there is just something special about the idea of a husband and wife walking together. I'm not sure why, but to me it has always spelled togetherness and harmony. Somehow, under that blue sky, amid God's exquisite handiwork, it felt unbearable to be walking alone.

As I trudged along, I began telling God all about it. Didn't He realize I had been a single adult for over ten years now? Surely He knew that Adam was not the only human who needed a companion! Why did He continually refrain from answering my prayer for a godly mate? Sometimes it was easy to accept God's path for me, but all too often it was just plain hard to walk alone.

Suddenly, in the quiet beauty of that winter day, God interrupted my grumbling with an arresting truth, "Child, if you are walking alone, how can you be talking to Me?"

Brought up short, I held my breath in amazement as the truth dawned on me. I was not alone—I was walking hand-in-hand with God Almighty, pouring out my woes into His listening ear! The wonder of it spread through me with a warm, gentle peace. Even if God should call me to finish my course on earth without a human companion, I could trust that I would always have Someone—God Himself!—to walk with me.

As I continued my walk through the snowy forest, I contemplated how we all experience feelings of loneliness, whether we are married or single, young or old. Under that vast blue sky, so hushed and serene, I came to a better comprehension that there is only One who can meet our greatest needs and fill our deepest longings. If we have peace with God through Jesus Christ and are living close to Him, not one of us is ever alone. Joy filled me as I realized we have an ever-present Father to lean on; a Friend to confide in; a Helper to bear our burdens; a Guide to lead us; and a Comforter to strengthen, console, and relieve. I finished my walk that winter day with a peaceful heart and deep contentment.

How good to walk with a Companion who is never too busy or

...Ordered Steps...

preoccupied to be with us! One who is never selfish or disinterested in even the minute details of our lives! We may tell Him our troubles, praise Him for His goodness, bring the needs of friends and family to Him, ask for direction, confess sin, and simply bask in the joy of His presence. Whether our path on earth is solitary or surrounded by loved ones, we need never fear that one step will be traveled alone. We have an omnipresent Friend to walk beside us—both now *and* through eternity!

The Lord

The Lord, in battle swift and strong;
The Lord, in might defeating wrong,
The Lord, whose hand holds everything—
He is my Helper and my King.

The Lord, who saves the seeking soul;
The Lord, who sin-sick hearts makes whole;
The Lord, whose love is deep and strong—
Is my Redeemer and my song.

The Lord, He has a perfect plan;
The Lord, He knows, He understands;
The Lord, whose Kingdom has no end—
He is my Father and my Friend.

...Ordered Steps...

"What if our eyes should be opened to see Jesus every time He is beside us, . . . *walking with us?* How radiant would all life then become! How many of us are conscious of the PRESENCE OF CHRIST WITH US, or get from it the full comfort, inspiration, and help which we might get?"

–J.R. Miller

"...THE LORD STOOD WITH ME, AND STRENGTHENED ME."
–II Timothy 4:7

"…Love as brethren,
be pitiful, be courteous."
I Peter 3:8

…Ordered Steps…

The Two Sides of Sensitivity

The sound of pleasant conversation buzzed around the room after the morning service. Ruth sighed, hesitating at the edge of a group of sisters near her age. Some days it was easy not to feel like a misfit, but today she struggled. With an effort, she brushed aside the feeling, cheerily greeting the sisters. She had known most of them since her childhood—and yet, how different her life seemed compared to theirs!

"Good morning, Ruth! How did your week go?" Elizabeth's warm greeting eased some of the tension in Ruth's heart.

"It went well," she replied with a smile, smoothing back blond curls from the forehead of Elizabeth's shy two-year-old, who clung to her mother's dress. "Busy, but good."

"Busy!" LeAnn chuckled at the word, shifting her chubby baby boy to her right shoulder, while patting his back with a loving hand.

"Ruth, you don't know what *busy* is until you've cared for three small children all day, mopped and cooked and cleaned, and been up with a teething infant countless nights! I feel ready to drop with fatigue."

No one seemed to notice the dark wave of color Ruth felt rolling up her neck and face. True, she didn't know what that was like, but she certainly felt willing to give it a try! Pain stabbed her heart and a lump seemed to fill her entire throat. How could LeAnn be so rude?

But everyone was laughing and murmurs of agreement were going around the group.

Mary commented, "My husband says he wants to get someone in to help for a day or so this week yet. I'm simply exhausted from trying to care for our four little ones, plus keeping the house in running order. Seems like I *never* get enough rest." She turned to Ruth. "Being a wife and mother is a blessing that I wouldn't trade for anything, but enjoy your full nights of sleep!"

Ruth winced involuntarily. "I'm sure it is a challenge to have such a house full," she managed to reply, hoping no one noticed the tremble in her voice, "but there's more to life than a good night's sleep."

"*Every* life has its challenges," a gentle voice interposed. "I know I have mine! But learning contentment in whatsoever state we are in is the key to peace." The voice belonged to a quiet little woman named Anna Martin. She and her husband had recently moved into the community. Ruth felt the depth of her words and gave her a grateful smile.

Later, at home, Ruth escaped to her room. Pulling her wicker rocker to the south window, she settled down in a patch of afternoon sunlight. The emotions inside of her were difficult to analyze. She sighed as she reviewed the incidents of that morning. She knew that LeAnn and Mary had not meant any harm with their comments; yet, oh, how it hurt to be continually reminded of the fact that she was thirty-two years old—and single. Instead of living in her own home, married and raising children, she was still where she'd always been—in her parents' home.

It wasn't that there hadn't been opportunities to marry, but God had firmly closed each door so far. Why, oh, why did everyone have to constantly refer to something that was out of her control?

It was true that she kept busy. God was faithful to fill her hands with worthwhile things. And yet, it was also true that she did not experience the challenges of being a wife and mother. It seemed because of that, most people considered her life of less importance. Tears burned against her eyelids as she squeezed her eyes shut. Why couldn't people be more understanding in their comments? Self-pity threatened to settle over her like a suffocating mist.

· · · · · · · · · · · · · · · · ·

Juice ran from under Ruth's knife as she halved and pitted another peach, adding the sticky fruit to a large bowl in front of her. It was enjoyable to be sitting in Anna Martin's bright kitchen, its many windows overlooking their large hayfield.

"Thanks so much for agreeing to help me can these peaches when I called this morning!" Anna was saying gratefully. "I'm afraid many of them would have spoiled if you hadn't been able to come!"

"I'm glad to do it," Ruth replied heartily. "I've been wanting to get to know you better, and this is a wonderful opportunity!"

They worked in companionable silence for a while, then Ruth asked, "So, you lived in Fairview before moving here, didn't you?"

"Yes, that's where I grew up," Anna explained. "James and I were renting a small farm there, but when this farm came to our attention, we were glad to purchase it!"

"Have you been married long?" Ruth asked.

"Well, it's been—oh, let me think—twelve years this January."

Twelve years! Ruth's knife paused in its work, and questions swept through her mind. Anna had been married for twelve years, and yet— She broke off her thoughts and reached for another peach. Her gaze traveled around the immaculate little farmhouse, its very cleanliness and quietness mutely proclaiming the absence of muddy little shoes, sticky fingers, and noisy little voices.

"You're wondering why there are no children, aren't you?" Anna asked quietly, interpreting Ruth's thoughts.

Ruth felt her face grow warm. "I—well, yes, I guess I *was* wondering," she admitted, lifting an embarrassed gaze to Anna's serene face. "But I don't mean to be nosy!"

"It's okay," Anna assured her. "I don't mind talking about it. You see, we found out early in our marriage that we could not have children. We have prayed that God would bless us with little ones, but we strive to be yielded to His will either way. Many people suggest adoption to us, but for several reasons, we haven't yet been able to pursue that."

"I'm sorry," Ruth said compassionately. "I'm sure it hasn't been an easy road for you, but I respect your attitude about it."

Anna smiled through tears that glistened in her dark eyes. "No, it hasn't been easy. Sometimes it is a daily struggle to accept God's will as best. But He is faithful to help us, and—" she paused meditatively, then continued. "I have learned that life isn't *meant* to be easy anyway. There will be aspects that bring deep grief to our hearts. After all, God tells us in His Word that each of us *will* experience tribulations. It is a part of His plan, and"—Anna smiled her gentle smile—"we certainly don't want to fight against God's plan for us."

For several minutes the only sound was the ticking of the kitchen clock and the slicing of peaches. Then Ruth asked, "Would you mind sharing what helped you have such a good attitude about your trials?

I mean, what are the things God has used to help you find peace? I'd like to know because I struggle myself!"

"Do you have all day to listen?" Anna asked, laughing. Then she sobered. "Well, let me see. First, accepting that God allows trials in our lives for a purpose—*that* has helped me the most." She went to the sink and rinsed her hands, her brow drawn together in thought. "Then, another main thing the Lord has taught me is about sensitivity. Did you ever think how there are two sides to that word?" she asked, returning to the table.

Ruth shook her head. "No, but you can tell me about it."

"Well, one side is being *personally* sensitive—touchy, you know. If someone makes an unkind or thoughtless remark to me about things that hurt me, I can easily find resentment and self-pity welling up inside."

"I know exactly what you mean," Ruth agreed. "But go on. I'm interested in hearing this."

"Um, let's see. Well, I think a good way to combat personal sensitivity is by not expecting others to fully understand." Anna paused. "I don't know if I'm making any sense to you," she went on, "but what I mean is this. I can't expect a mother to completely understand the grief of barrenness any more than she can expect me to understand the fatigue of—well, staying up nights with a teething baby, or trying to discipline a strong-willed child, or grieving over a wayward teen. We can—and should!—sympathize with each other; but never having *been* there, we can't be expected to fully understand."

"That's true—and rather a new thought to me," Ruth confessed. "I guess I expect people to automatically know which comments will hurt me."

Anna was nodding her head. "That's how it has been for me too. But when I realize others can't be expected to fully understand *my* pain any more than I can *theirs*, it helps me not to be upset by thoughtless things they might say. Then I'm not so—well, so *in tune* to my feelings, so touchy. Others will be able to talk freely around me without having to worry about stepping on my toes."

"That makes sense," Ruth agreed slowly. Then she grinned sheepishly at Anna. "I *know* it would make me a more pleasant person to be around! I'm far too touchy. I need to think seriously about all of this."

"There's another aspect too," Anna said. "Often someone will say something to me that they think is kind and helpful, but instead it causes pain. I've learned—and am *still* learning!—that I have a choice in how I receive such words. I can be offended, or I can realize they were meant kindly, and so be blessed and helped by the motive behind them."

They worked silently for a while, then Ruth asked, "Okay, what's the *other* side to sensitivity?"

"This one is hardest for me," Anna admitted. "It's learning to be sensitive to others' pain. While we shouldn't let their thoughtless remarks bother us, we should be careful not to be thoughtless ourselves. I remember when one of my cousins had a child with Down's syndrome. My first words to her were, 'Oh, no!' Later she confided to me that those words had hurt. I think of that often when others accidentally wound my heart. Usually they are just as innocent as I was of wanting to cause pain."

Ruth winced. She thought of the times she had downplayed LeAnn's weariness, or secretly scoffed over Mary's struggle to keep all four children under control. Careless comments she had made to them on these subjects suddenly paraded across her mind. "Ouch, that goes deep," she said regretfully to Anna. "I can remember instances when I've spoken thoughtlessly too."

"That's where my biggest problem lies," Anna agreed. "I still have to ask for the Lord's help often in that area."

"You've given me a lot to think about!" Ruth commented. "Thank you for sharing. It helps."

Soon the conversation drifted to other topics, but Ruth knew that she would never forget Anna's wise counsel.

"Thank you so much for helping me today!" Anna said later as Ruth prepared to leave.

"No," Ruth returned seriously. "Thank *you* for helping *me*! You've been a real encouragement to me."

That evening Ruth had much to ponder. Sensitivity. It certainly was something that could be good or bad, depending on how it was applied! Too often she was acutely in tune to her own pain, yet heedless of others' trials. And wasn't that exactly what bothered her about others' treatment of herself! "Lord," she prayed softly, "I am sorry! I have been so self-centered! Help me to learn to be sensitive to others' trials, more careful with my words and less touchy of theirs!"

Ruth prepared for sleep that night with a lighter heart than she'd had for many weeks. With God's help, things would be different from now on.

Common Dust

The way is long, the path severe *(I Tim. 6:12; II Tim. 2:3)*,
All we are weak who travel here *(Matt. 26:41)*;
Tired and footsore, prone to fall *(Matt. 26:69-75)*:
This is our frame—not one, but all *(Psalm 103:14)*.
We also fail; let us be kind *(Eph. 4:32)*!
Be of a compassionate mind *(Matt. 18:23-35)*!

Easy to take the lofty mind *(Luke 18:10-14)*,
Mark others' faults, to ours be blind *(Matt. 7:1-5)*;
Judge when we've never had to go
The roughness of the path they know *(Job 16:1-5)*.
Oh, this is not the way of love *(I Cor. 13:1-8)*!
This is not the wisdom from above *(James 3:17)*!

Take heed, oh self, unless you fall *(Prov. 16:18; I Cor. 9:27)*,
For I am weak, and I am small *(II Cor. 3:5)*.
A member of the human race *(Titus 3:1-7; Isaiah 64:6)*—
Nothing, but for saving grace *(Ps. 115:1; Eph. 2:8-9)*.
May knowledge of Christ's righteousness *(Romans 5:17)*
Chasten my heart to true meekness *(Eph. 4:1-3)*.
Amen.

...Ordered Steps...

"Enjoying each other's good is heaven begun."
–L.C. Smith

"All extreme sensitiveness, fastidiousness,
suspicion, readiness to take offense, and tenacity
of what we think our due, come from self-love."
–Jean Nicolas Grou

"A NEW COMMANDMENT I GIVE
UNTO YOU, That ye love one another; as I
have loved you, that ye also love one another."
–John 13:34

"For he knoweth our frame;"
he remembereth that we are dust."
Psalm 103:14

"But [he] made himself of no reputation, and
took upon him the form of a servant, and
was made in the likeness of men."
Philippians 2:7

...Ordered Steps...

18

Out of the Dust

Sometimes life isn't very fun. That day especially. My cherished hopes had been dashed to pieces, and I found myself up against painful rejection. To top it off, the frowning sky was busy weeping drizzly tears over everything. Not very cheering when you are feeling down! I paced the house from window to window, feeling the confines of the four walls. Finally, rain or no rain, I *had* to get out.

The cool breeze did a good job blowing cobwebs from my mind, and misty rain pummeling my face brought me keenly awake. Yet still the pain churned inside. As I sloshed through the grass and mud in soggy tennis shoes, I looked up at the sky. Even God seemed far away. Tears mingled with the rain on my cheeks. Of course, in my heart I knew God had allowed this pain for a reason, but somehow that knowledge didn't ease the hurt. Never before had I felt so worthless and insignificant. "Lord," I whispered, "do You know what? I feel like nothing more than a lump of dirt today."

I have often wondered why God ever took up that dust and formed a creature in His image. I've wondered why He breathed into him the breath of life, an eternal soul. So many times it's hard to see past the dust and into the eternal purpose of the Sovereign Ruler of all things. Life can take on a pointless outlook on occasion. "Lord, why did You make us, anyway? We experience—and cause!—so much pain. Your world was so beautiful without us! Wouldn't it have been better to skip humans?"

But God knew what He was doing. There is a solid reason, a perfect plan, and a great purpose to our creation and to the circumstances He allows in the lives of His children. He sees beyond our frame of dust, and orchestrates each pain, each joy, each step, viewing the eternal.

Now, that's wonderful! But I think there is an even *better* aspect: God, who formed our frame of dust, looks with compassionate love upon it. It's not simply what He sees in the *eternal future* that moves His heart to love us—we are valuable to Him *now*, dust and all. So valuable, beyond comprehension, that He sent His only Son to come down among us, clothe Himself in our human clay, understand by experience our frame, and through His sacrifice ransom us from its fetters.

Yet how was that love received? Many scoffed, hated, and turned away from Christ. It still happens today! He who left His glory to take on our dust so we may have the choice to spend eternity with Him met pain, rejection, and death. Why do I expect a different road?

That day of weeping clouds was not fun. I walked and cried and wondered, "Why, Lord?" The beauty of His answer didn't penetrate right away. I walked many cloudy days before the sun broke through and healing came. But through it all He helped me to better see the wideness of His mercy and the vastness of His love for human clay.

...*Ordered Steps*...

He chose the pain so that we could have a way to receive His healing love. He took on our frame so that, coming to Him, we may be lifted out of the dust.

Since He chose to do so much for us, let us choose to trustfully yield to what He allows in our lives—even if it be the pain of rejection.

> *I shy the spear,*
> *The pointed nails,*
> *The smiting and the stripes;*
> *Yet You who could have saved Yourself*
> *Yielded up Your life.*
> *"Is a servant better than his Master?"*
> *No, Lord, it could not be.*
> *"Then accept the hurt and pain, child,*
> *Even as Me."*

for Me

"Rejected"—such an ugly little word!
Torn, bruised, and beaten: this, my loving Lord!
When You had planned to give us all—yet we
In foolish blindness nailed You to the tree.
You walked this earth in goodness; all You touched
Were healed, made whole, cheered, and lifted up.
No sin or fault could any find in You—
The pure and spotless One, full good, full true.
And yet, *for this* You came to walk the earth.
Yes, *this* the very reason for Your birth!
To leave Your glory, die a painful death;
To rise in mercy, to restore and bless!
I, guilty, all unworthy, lost in sin,
May through Your awesome love be born again.
O Master—such great love! Blessed mystery!
When You were crucified, *it was for me!*

"…We have this treasure in earthen vessels, that the *excellency of the power* may be of God, and not of us."

–II Corinthians 4:7

Indwelling

There is no power, Lord, nor could there be
In this frail dust—unless You breathe in me.
I am an earthen vessel; You are God
Almighty, yet You stoop to make this clod
All glorified by filling me with You–
A channel for Your power to shine through.

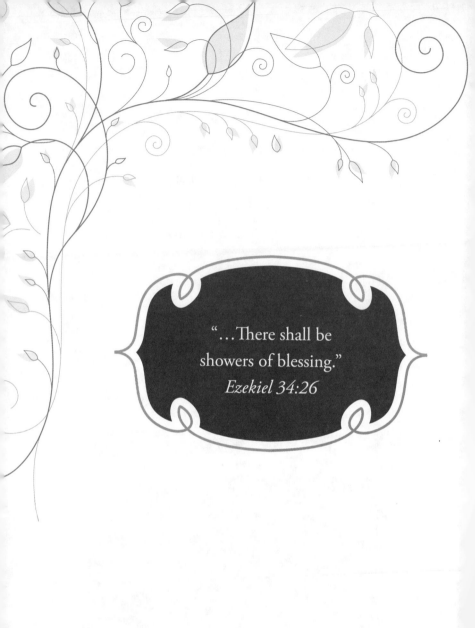

"…There shall be
showers of blessing."
Ezekiel 34:26

…Ordered Steps…

19

Grass in the Field

Would you like to take a walk with me this balmy spring morning, washed new by early rain? Let's bring an old quilt to sit on after we stroll to the top of that hill. Ah, what a view! Take a deep breath—isn't the air invigorating? Listen to the sweet sound of birdsong reverberating on all sides. And see how the sun is shining through breaks in the clouds, flooding the lush, cross-fenced fields with warmth and light!

Yes, you're right. There *are* some dry areas down there, bristling with thorns and thistles; and I do see a few outcroppings of rocks. But don't you agree what catches your eye the most is the abundance of that one paradoxical color—both soothing and energizing—*green?* Like luxurious carpeting, new grass has spread across the earth in vibrant hues. There's no way to fully describe the beauty of it!

But stop—look over there! An illustration of the proverbial "the grass is greener on the other side"! That huddle of cows is crowding the fence, struggling to reach juicy blades of grass on the other side, while just a little bit down the fence line another herd is standing in *that* juicy grass, trying to reach the tender green the other bovine are standing in! How ignorant can they get?

Well, cows are merely—cows! Of course they'll act foolish. They can't help it that God didn't create them with much discernment. And since they aren't standing on this hill overlooking the fields, they can't see that the grass is equally green across *all* the fields, on *both* sides of the fence! I'm glad we humans aren't that silly.

Or are we?

Here I am on the "singlehood" side of the fence, looking longingly across to the luxuriant green of the blessings on the "married" side.

·A good, hardworking husband to provide for his family; godly and strong for his wife to lean on and be a helper to.

·Love and romance under the smile of God.

·The oneness of an exclusive relationship where you stick together forever and walk beside one another as best friends and sweethearts.

·A home to keep, where a family all your own finds rest and joy.

·Precious children all your own to love and raise for the glory of God.

·A special family unit ordained and blessed by God.

How wonderful! There's no way to fully describe the beauty of a godly marriage! Yet here I am in my "singlehood" field—which I assure you is a terribly dry spot of thorns, thistles, and rocks—feeling starved to death viewing all that luscious green over there! How unfair that I'm stuck where everything is so ugly and tasteless.

I don't like being alone; earning money to provide for myself; not having any children; missing out on married love; and experiencing all of those painful emotions that inevitably come when a friend has another child or a couple twelve years younger than I is planning their wedding.

...Ordered Steps...

I dread how uncomfortable the next six weeks will be while our minister is giving his series on marriage. I feel like an oddball when Mother's Day comes around and all the wives and moms are recognized and commended. I'd love to be a keeper at home, following Titus 2:4-5 with joy—but I'm not in that "field," so I can't. And the list of grievances about my "field" goes on.

Still, while I'm straining to peer through the fence again, I begin to see something not-so-luxurious on the other side. Struggles to submit to the husband; disagreements over certain issues; human nature causing friction and pain; financial difficulties due to the bad economy or because the husband had an injury and can't work; little irritations that come from living in close proximity to the same person 24/7; a strong-willed child; morning sickness; interrupted sleep; only approximately ten full minutes of privacy a day; excess pounds that won't come off after yet another pregnancy—well! I guess that, amid the lovely green of blessings, there are also some dry spots, thorns, thistles, and rocks on the *married* side of the fence too!

Contentment. I've read that it is a choice we make, regardless of the "field" we find ourselves in. After viewing the two sides of this fence, I can only say, "How true!" No set of circumstances is either perfect or despicable. If we are seeking to obey and follow God, He is faithful to send showers of blessings no matter which field He has placed us in. We will find ourselves knee-deep in lush green, if we will simply take the time to look!

Yes, admittedly there are aspects of singlehood that I don't enjoy— dry spots, thorns, thistles, and rocks that I simply am *not* fond of. But those aspects are merely a part of the whole. Certainly a God-ordained marriage is something I desire; but until God sets me in that "field," I must find contentment in the one He *has* placed me in, feeding on the abundant blessings there.

·I'm able to get up early and have devotions, communing with my Savior and God in the quiet of the dawn.

·I can do my daily exercises without interruptions and without feeling like I'm neglecting family or other duties.

·In my free time, I can take long, invigorating walks every day.

·If I need to go shopping or run errands, I simply get ready and go!

·I can pursue hobbies that I would never have the time for as a married woman.

·I have the freedom to make the ultimate decisions in my life.

·I am able to be part of an outreach ministry to children, that is best done by someone without young children of their own.

·I can write for hours—even in the middle of the night!—without bothering anyone.

·I have more time in my day to spend interceding for family and friends.

And the list goes on. Once I started looking, there's no way to fully describe the beauty of it!

No matter what our circumstances, our loving Father is sure never to forget or neglect us. He has promised to shower us with blessings, rich and green—and He does! Yes, even on the "singlehood" side of the fence. I think it's time I turned my gaze away from the grass on the "married" side, and set myself to discover the sweetness of what is growing *even* here.

"Ask ye of the LORD rain…, so the LORD shall make bright clouds, and give them showers of rain, to *every one*"—not just married folks!—"grass in the field" (Zechariah 10:1, emphasis mine).

"I have learned, in whatsoever state I am, therewith to be content" (Philippians 4:11).

"Remember this, had any other condition been better for you than the one in which you are, divine love would have put you there."
–C.H. Spurgeon,
Evening by Evening, October 11

"We do trust our God; we do believe that if there had been anything better than what is, that better thing would have been chosen for us."
–Amy Carmichael,
Edges of His Ways, August 28

"Remember that wherever you are, you are put there by God."
–Oswald Chambers,
My Utmost for His Highest, August 30

"Be ye also patient;
stablish your hearts: for
the coming of the Lord draweth nigh."
James 5:8

"Behold, I come quickly."
Revelation 22:7

...Ordered Steps...

20

"I'll Be Back Soon!"

It had been a hard day for two-year-old Rose Anna. Mother was away and Aunt Betty was taking care of her. "I'll be back soon," Mother had promised. "Be good for Aunt Betty while I'm gone."

Rose Anna tried to be good. She loved Aunt Betty very much, but somehow no one could compare to Mama!

When Rose Anna stubbed her bare toe on the bedroom doorjamb, Aunt Betty did her best to console her—but her tearful cry was, "I want Mama!" Then there had been nap time. How impossible to close her eyes and relax when Mama was away!

Oh, yes, she had experienced some fun times during the day too, but always Rose Anna had Mama in her thoughts. When Aunt Betty helped her draw a picture, her first thought was, "I want to show Mama!" When Aunt Betty praised her for picking up her toys, Rose Anna knew Mama would be glad too. After a happy walk through the woods, she burst in the front door, ready to share her adventures with Mama—but Mama wasn't there yet.

Now dusk was falling and tears rolled down Rose Anna's cheeks. When would Mama come? The sound of gravel crunching under car tires met her ears. With a glad cry she ran to the window, straining to see Mama's familiar figure step out of the car. In minutes she was clasped in her mother's arms. All the loneliness and hurt of the day suddenly faded from her mind. The one Rose Anna loved best had finally come.

Sometimes I feel a bit like Rose Anna. The One I love best is away, but He promised that He will soon return. I know He will keep His word, yet sometimes it is hard to wait.

Unlike when earthly dear ones are separated, my Most Beloved is still with my spirit. Though I cannot see or speak to Him face-to-face, He communes with me through His Word and listens to my prayers. His presence is ever with me. Many times He shows His care for me through the Church. He understands my tears; He sympathizes with my loneliness. Always He watches over me and is ready to listen to my sorrows and joys.

But now dusk is falling and there are tears on my cheeks. How I miss my Lord! I find myself longing more than ever to actually see His dear face, hear His voice, and forever be safe and secure in His arms.

What is this I hear? The signs of the times are like gravel crunching under approaching wheels. My spirit leaps for joy and I strain my eyes upward. All the hurt and loneliness of the day will soon be swept away when I am clasped in His arms. What a wonderful anticipation—the One I love best is coming back soon!

"Even so, come, Lord Jesus" (Revelation 22:20).

...Ordered Steps...

All Through

I said, "My Father, this is such a long
And weary road—how can I make it through
Each slow, slow step? What if I make a wrong
Turn, dear Lord? *Oh, I want Home and You!*"

My Father said: "Your days are fleeting ones—
    Eternity is long, but time is not.
    It isn't many more dawning of suns
You'll greet, and I have numbered to your lot
    Precise amounts of seconds. No delay
Will interfere with plans I made for you—
    Believe each promise and each word I say,
Trust Me to help you every step, all through:
Someday I will be coming, *child, for you!*

...*Ordered Steps*...